Forty-Seven Stories of Jesus

You have probably never heard

By Aaron

Channeled by Barbara Brodsky

Edited and arranged by William Altork

Forty-Seven Stories of Jesus
You have probably never heard

First printing 2009
Second revised printing 2013

Front and back cover photos by Michael Forster Rothbart
www.mfrphoto.com

Published by:
Deep Spring Press
P. O. Box 6052
Ann Arbor, Michigan
48106-6052
Telephone: (734) 971-3455
Email: DeepSpringPressBooks@gmail.com

Printed in the United States by
Sheridan Books, Inc., Chelsea, Michigan
ISBN: 978-0-9745552-2-5

Books can be ordered directly from Deep Spring Press at a
cost of $17.00 ($14 for the book and $3 mailing charge) or
purchased on-line at Amazon.com.

Table of Contents

Preface

by William Altork

This is a book of stories about Jesus. These stories did not come from the Bible. They were channeled (I hesitate to use that word, because its use has become so cliché), by my dear and loving friend Barbara Brodsky and her deeply spiritual companion, Aaron. I present this material for the sole purpose of helping to awaken our sense of divinity and to actively inspire us with love and compassion toward one another.

In my younger years, the Bible and Christianity were forced upon me in a discouraging manner. I know there are many others who have had similar experiences. The older, more traditional ways of expressing Christianity simply do not inspire us as they could. In large part, because of those early negative impressions, I came to realize my permanent bond with Christ rather late in life. Even then, it happened only after I came to understand that it was acceptable with God for me to think and believe 'outside the box.'

For me, Christ is central to my core beliefs. He is my guide and the Father is the source of my spiritual journey. Each time I read through Aaron's stories about Jesus, I find myself immersed in the grace of Jesus' teachings and His deep, deep love. So I wish to share them with you, and hope that you may experience the same. While reading them, I ask only one thing of you. Regardless of the source, please allow your heart to respond openly to the stories. If they resonate with you then please press on. If not, that is okay. Any additional comments that Aaron may offer will precede or follow the stories. These stories span a period of approximately fifteen years and are taken from transcripts of Aaron's talks. As Aaron says, please consider their content with the language of your heart.

Before I share Barbara's discovery of and subsequent friendship with Aaron, I must tell you that, although I do not consider myself to be a skeptic, I use discretion when considering the authenticity of messengers from the other side. I fully accept that times have changed, and that at this point it would be foolish to dismiss all possibilities of Divine communication through other sources. Today many people have become accustomed to thinking and exploring more openly than in preceding generations. In much of our modern day culture, it is common to apply new and more liberal considerations in seeking answers to the age-old mysteries of life and our relationship with God.

One rainy day while my wife was enjoying an afternoon in Ann Arbor, she literally slipped on one of Barbara's flyers inside the entrance of a store. After she threw it away there was another one stuck to the bottom of her shoe. She considered that to be more than a coincidence, so she picked it up and read it. When she got home she shared her story and the flyer with me. Shortly after that we decided to go visit Barbara.

We spent the next two years meeting every other week at Barbara's home with a small group to meditate and listen to Aaron speak to us through Barbara. Not only did we become friends with Barbara, but even more remarkably, we easily grew to trust and love Aaron. Within a short time it became clear to us that Aaron was quite real, as well as very wise, thoughtful and loving.

Aaron does not discuss the trivia of daily living. He does not tell fortunes or predict future events. He would not help you decide which apartment to rent; if you and your loved-one were soul-mates; which job to seek; or whether or not you will win the lottery. With any of the mundane, self-gratifying surface questions Aaron would simply and lovingly steer us toward discovering a greater place of love and understanding in ourselves. He was always challenging us to think, act and live more skillfully. Many years have passed since then. As I look back on those days, however, the truth of his gracious wisdom and love lives within me still.

You may contact William Altork at: billaltork@gmail.com

An Introduction to Barbara and Aaron

by Barbara Brodsky

I suddenly lost my hearing in 1972 after my first child was born. In those early years of my deafness, I struggled a lot with anger and fear. Why did this happen to me? This is not fair! When alone, I learned to cope with it well, but when I saw people together talking, I would shut down. There was so much grasping on my part; a need to know what they were saying.

So the years passed. More space developed in my awareness, and I was able to handle the deafness adequately. In some ways I became a super mom; I had two more children, and was teaching sculpture at the University of Michigan. I had a loving husband, close friends, and a very full and rich life. But I knew there was something under there that I needed to understand. I was shutting myself out of some life experiences, and was still closing down.

Finally, I prayed for help. I don't know what kind of help I was expecting. I had been meditating regularly since 1960; but I certainly didn't know anything about channeling. One morning I was sitting in my living room meditating when suddenly I saw a being in front of me: he shone with radiant white light, and I could feel his energy the way you feel energy when your back is to the doorway, but you can still feel someone enter the room.

I was very startled and said, "Who are you? What is this?" I got up and walked out of the room, not waiting for an answer. I went to the kitchen and got a cup of tea. I thought, maybe I'm hallucinating. But at some level I knew that was not so. I almost wished it were not real, because it would have been easier than the alternative of facing this peculiar reality.

I came back and meditated. He was still there, so I just sat there with his energy. The next day he was there, waiting for me to return. I noted his presence more clearly: a brilliant white light; so bright that I could not tell if the light shone from him or if he was sitting in the middle of a white sun. His piercing blue eyes radiated with the clarity and depth of crystalline water. He had a gentle face, white beard and flowing, snow-white hair.

Aaron calls himself a being of light. He is a discarnate entity, which means that he has gone beyond the life and death cycles of the human body. There had been little in my life to prepare me for such an encounter.

"Who are you?" I asked.

"I am your teacher," came the reply. "You asked for help. I am here to help."

His energy was so calm and loving and present. There was no push for me to do anything. He was just there. It took me a few days to move past my discomfort; I had to resolve my old opinions of new-age mumbo-jumbo, and I contemplated the possibility that this was a hallucination. Day by day, as I meditated, he waited quietly. I never felt pulled or pushed to accept him. I thought, if you suspect a hallucination, but it doesn't go away, at what point do you consider it to be real and then investigate further? My heart repeatedly told me to trust.

Finally I said, "Okay. What are you here to teach me?"

He said, "You are suffering. Let's start there. Let's look at the nature of the suffering."

Indeed I was suffering. He took me on an amazing journey to understand that the deafness was not the cause of the suffering, but rather it was the anger about the deafness; and my grasping and thinking, "I shouldn't be deaf. It's not fair!"

As I made more peace with the deafness I began to realize that it was just the experience of deafness: ears that don't hear. That's all it was. I began to see how the anger was related to a fear that I wouldn't be safe. I realized more each day that I could simply allow myself to be deaf.

About three months into this experience, I went to a meditation workshop run by Stephen Levine. I wrote to him ahead of time and said, "I'm deaf and am not coming to hear your workshop; I'm coming to not hear your workshop." He understood exactly what I meant by that, that I was coming just to be there and watch all the grasping that came up; the need to hear. I truly knew there was nothing he was saying that

I needed to hear; that at some level I already knew all he was sharing.

So I went and I watched him, and of course the first day grasping came up, "I'm going to miss something! I've got to get it! Something's going by and it's just what I needed. I'm going to miss it!" The second day was easier. By the third day the miracle was not that I could hear, but that there was just somebody deaf sitting there and just somebody on the platform talking. There was no grasping any more. I was able to sit there, feeling sad sometimes that I couldn't hear, but without a lot of fear.

After I returned home, people started asking me if they could talk to Aaron. I said, "I suppose so." At first there were just "yes" and "no" answers, and then gradually; longer answers. I said, "I don't know how to do this."

Aaron said, "Just be quiet. Hear what I am saying and speak it out."

So I did. Somebody said, "Oh, you're channeling!"

"What's channeling?" I said. I still didn't really know what channeling was.

It's grown from there. That was a long time ago. We started with half-a-dozen people in my living room, teaching them the meditation that Aaron was teaching me; and also with me channeling Aaron. And now we have a big organization, Deep Spring Center for Meditation and Spiritual Inquiry. There are many meditation teachers. We have a wonderful board of directors, rotating every few years so that many people will have an opportunity to do this work. There are many classes. It's been wonderful to watch this process of growth and learning for all.

Is Aaron real? I cannot answer that. I can only tell you how I experience him and share his message as clearly as I am able. Aaron teaches us to, "Listen with your heart and not your brain." He asks us to consider the substance of the message and whether it confirms our own deepest truth. "Do these words help you to live your lives with more wisdom and love?" he queries. "If not, then just lay them aside. The source is irrelevant. Please consider the content. Listen and interpret what I have to say with the language of your heart."

My deepest thanks to my dear friend Bill Altork, for spending endless hours going through innumerable pages of transcripts to make these stories more accessible; and for his first publication of them. Thanks to Lalita Doke for her clear editing that makes this edition even more free of errors; and to my husband Hal Rothbart, and my friend Nicholas de Paul, for their help in producing the republished version, that you see here.

With Love,
Barbara Brodsky

More information on Barbara and more material from Aaron, including the original, longer stories from which these 47 stories have been excerpted, can be found through the Deep Spring Center in Ann Arbor, Michigan, at www.deepspring.org. There you will find extensive archives, all of which are freely downloadable. See: **archives > Aaron > special topics > Christmas Stories**, for the full list of Christmas Stories.

Many more details about Barbara's first meeting and early experiences with Aaron are in her book, *Cosmic Healing: A Spiritual Journey with Aaron and John of God*, North Atlantic Books, Berkeley, California, 2011.

Numerous other books from Barbara and Aaron are also available from Deep Spring Center, your local bookstore, or on Amazon.

Barbara accepts no direct fees for her work. She welcomes donations, which can be mailed to her through Deep Spring Center. Your donations allow her to devote her full time to her work with Aaron.

Foreword & Introduction to The Stories

by Aaron

[Compiled from several of Aaron's talks]

At the time of Jesus' birth I was a young child living in the hills near Bethlehem with my father who was a shepherd, as well as a teacher in the nearby spiritual community. As an adult I became a shepherd. I was also deeply trained in spiritual practices. I had a great love for Jesus, much gratitude that our paths had connected, and appreciation for His teachings. As an adult I came to this beloved Friend and Master, and followed Him whenever I could. The following is an introductory perspective on my times spent with Jesus, gathered from talks I have offered.

Do you understand what the birth of Jesus really means; who He was and what was truly given? God offered His Son to this world in order to speak to the immense suffering here. It is fine for you to relate to Jesus as the Son of God, literally, if that is of help to you. But, although He was among the most perfectly evolved Beings to ever live on earth, do not limit yourself and assume that He is the only Son of God. Allow yourself reverence for life in all its multitudes of forms, both here on earth and throughout the universe. Even more, if you see God in Jesus, then you must see God in everything. However you relate to Jesus, please be aware of the amazing love that prompted Him to incarnate among us.

It is not my intention to offend anyone, but there is much confusion between the true gift of Jesus and the church doctrine that has grown up around His life. Each religion establishes its own mythology, which is at times helpful in fostering the faith of those who find nurturance in that religion. But, that same mythology can also hinder a more modern and realistic approach on one's journey towards God. How Jesus was born does not change at all the essence of His life and death here on earth. Jesus was a fully realized Being. He incarnated here only to serve and to teach. One who would move into such an incarnation in this way must do so through a pure source. Mary's heart was pure and she was capable of teaching her child what it needed to know so that it could fully develop the potential within that incarnation. For that we thank and bless her.

The highest intention at the time of Jesus' coming was the opening of the earth plane to higher consciousness. For many millennia the earth plane had been in a lower consciousness in which people were disconnected. Jesus' coming was meant to open the door to higher consciousness; to help people begin to know their interconnectedness with each other and with the earth, because only through that knowing can there truly be love.

You are all one heart! Not knowing this, it is easier to kill others and take from them for your own needs. But once you understand, can you kill and take from yourself?

The beauty of Jesus' gift is such that it needs no myths to support it. Like all of you, Jesus lived through many incarnations. Long, long ago He moved past the cycle of birth and death. He, like you, moved from dwelling on the shadow within toward an awareness of the inherent expression of the Divine. His learning experiences eventually brought Him into perfection with God: the Core Essence of you and me and all of creation.

It is sad that you cannot know all of Jesus' many incarnation experiences, and be thus inspired with your own growth by understanding His progression. Long ago He was at the same experiential level that you are today. He has been who you are. He has lived through all the lives and personal experiences that you could possibly imagine. That is why He loves you so and is capable of fully understanding you and offering perfect love back to you.

As God is fully expressed in Jesus, the seed of God in you is ever-expanding toward that same perfection. You are all sparks of God, evolving through your many lifetimes toward perfect light and mature compatibility with your Creator. Since the dawn of time a few beings have so evolved as to become pure and radiant light, filling the universe with their luminescence. Such Beings truly sit at the side of God, and the power of their light and love are inextinguishable.

Jesus is such a Being. For God, Jesus was the proof of His Divine plan; the perfect example of what all mankind could become. As such He was deeply beloved − the Son of God − as you are all sons and daughters of God. Jesus was especially cherished because He was among the first to reach this Divine perfection.

Your world in those days was full of war, misunderstanding, hatred and chaos even more than now. Many people of that time believed that God taught them to avenge themselves on others, as well as one nation to another. Much bloodshed was enacted in the name of God. Many believed that God's laws were a matter of convenience; that murder was permitted in His name. These were not people meaning to do evil, but beings filled with misunderstandings. The emotional climate then was very different than it is today. Yes, there is war and hatred in many parts of the world today. But today there is also a word the concept of which scarcely existed two thousand years ago, and that word is forgiveness. The prevailing philosophy then was an eye for an eye and a tooth for a tooth.

Seeing the misunderstandings that filled the world, God grieved for His children. So He asked His Son, who stood by His side, to give a great gift to mankind; to take it unto Himself to return to that human plane to teach lessons of love, compassion and forgiveness. The gift was no less God's, for He was giving His beloved Son unto the pain and chaos of the physical world.

The spirit of the man you know as Jesus agreed to God's request, with gladness that He might serve Him. He fully understood that in returning to this physical plane and incarnating in human form, He was taking on all the pains of being human. He agreed to the forgetting of His true self. Although this forgetting did not go as deep as with most humans, He did experience times of deep doubt and despair. He agreed to the physical pains of the human body and the frailty of the human form. The nails that penetrated His flesh at His crucifixion were extremely painful. Out of love, and to give love, He gladly accepted whatever agony He might face.

Jesus came to teach God's true message of love and peace to a weary, chaotic, pain-filled world. He came to teach humans that they are essentially spirit, expressing through the body and mind; and to remind them never to forget their Divine Essence. He came to teach humans that we mirror the Divine Consciousness of God, if we will choose to do so, and that we do have free will choice. This is the true gift of His birth and His life.

He had free will, as have all beings. He could have said no and God would not have loved Him any less. Do you understand what it means to freely and willingly leave that perfect light and love? Can you understand how much this Holy Spirit loved mankind and God to accept this mission of teaching? Only perfect love could have made this choice, and only perfect love would have been able to teach such love to others. Which of you could send a beloved child of your own to a place torn by war and hatred, to certain agony, to teach others?

As you think about Jesus and His teachings of love and peace and forgiveness, think also about the gift given: perfect love. Let all Christmas gifts and your human gifts be love and forgiveness to one another so that Jesus may see that His lessons are truly being learned. This is the greatest gift you can give Him; the way you can best honor His gift: to love one another.

Jesus continues to give His gift of love. For a long time He has been fully qualified to move on and be even closer with God. But He holds back from doing so to continue to keep His energy available to us. When all suffering is done on earth, I believe Jesus will go home. But meanwhile, He remains present and available. This is His on-going gift.

An important aspect of Jesus' teachings is that forgiveness must begin with yourself and then be extended out to others; that you don't need to suffer in a mythical hell for your sins, but you create your own hell by holding on to separation and judgment. This is not hard to understand: you cannot harm another or your self and have it go unnoticed. Each time you do harm to another you must truly repent of that harm and ask forgiveness of that being. Atonement (at-one-ment) comes to you when you have understood the harm you have done and you have asked for forgiveness. But you are still responsible for what you have done and you will experience the consequences of your actions.

There is a belief among some Christians that you can heap this karma on Jesus' shoulders; that He died for your sins and in His blanket forgiveness you are relieved from all consequence. Perhaps this is where the Christian concept of salvation derives. I see this as a distortion. Salvation is to be found, not through the acts of Jesus (and other Masters), but through following His teachings and becoming responsible for yourself. Your salvation is in your readiness to follow His teachings of love and forgiveness; to begin to sow these new seeds. He shows you the path to salvation but He doesn't do it for you. He guides you so that you may do it for yourselves.

Jesus experienced both joy and pain in His life. Once He incarnated on this earth He was human just like you and me. But the veil that separated Him from His true spiritual identity was far less dense than it is for most of you. Thus, He truly understood that God was his Father, and the Essence of His being. I wish the listener to understand that I do not use Father or Him in reference to God as a masculine identity here, but only to simplify the phrasing. God as Divine Source is Father and Mother, Him and Her.

Jesus understood His relationship with that Divinity even as a young boy. Some of you may be familiar with this story from the Bible: When he was in Jerusalem for the Passover with Mary and Joseph, he was separated from them. Eventually they found Him talking to learned men at the temple. In response to His parent's questions of concern and worry He replied,

"I must be about my Father's business." And yet in His human-ness, especially in His early years, He felt physical pain and experienced the same doubts and fears as any other person. In the end He suffered real pain. And yet His final words were, "Forgive them, Father."

Can you see what would have happened to His life and His teachings if He had been proclaimed a prince or a teacher, to be loved and never feared in any way; to have built up great wealth and a following, and then died peacefully as an old man? How much less influence would His teachings have had? It is easy to say, "Forgive them," when there is little to forgive. But to be there on that cross in agony and still be able to say, "Forgive them," is deeply inspiring.

Jesus did not take your sins unto Himself so much as He led the way for you. His crucifixion was offered as your salvation in terms of its being the most profound way of giving His message. He had a choice, as you always have a choice. He did not have to die in that way. But He understood that His death was as important as His life, and that this was the gift He was asked to give. He gave it joyfully that others could receive His message and understand it.

Forgiveness is not meant just for the routine errors of life, but more so when there is everything to lose and everything to forgive. Once you have understood and mastered that lesson, this cycle of birth and death you are in is broken, because forgiveness truly ends karma. This is the gift of salvation that His teaching offers.

I knew Jesus as a boy and also knew Him many years later toward the end of His life, when I followed Him and He was my teacher. I was still a shepherd, though also a respected member of the community where we both lived at times. At that stage of His life He neither felt nor expressed anger. And yet, I feel sure that as a younger man, He did experience anger. I emphasize that this is conjecture, not directly from His teachings, but from my own present understanding about anger. He accepted His humanness. His anger, I would think, was not personalized so that it became Him; not fixated upon, but was simply felt as an impersonal emotion. I sense that He felt anger and, for that matter, joy without aversion or attachment. Even while He was feeling anger, through the depth of His compassion and understanding, He was able to forgive those beings who angered Him. He understood why they felt the way they did; why they needed to behave as they did, and, no less importantly, He forgave Himself for permitting anger to arise.

He was angered, I feel certain, by injustice and callousness. But it was so totally balanced by love that it created no long-held contraction or distortion. He was unique. Very few beings are born into human bodies and are as highly evolved as He was in that lifetime. He had no need to incarnate for His own growth. He accepted this work purely out of love and to serve others.

Obviously, most of you are not that evolved. You are here to learn. And so, simultaneously you feel anger and you understand that there is a need to forgive, to put yourself in the other person's shoes and know their fears. But the anger is still personalized. That is fine. You are here to learn; you are not expected to be perfect. Achieving this awareness can be accelerated by using the guiding life of Jesus as an example. It is a process you will need to repeat over and over, each time accepting that you are human. As long as you are here incarnate and learning in a human body, there are going to be anger and other heavy emotions.

Jesus was born the Christ; fully alive. And yet He was human. As He matured, the veil became more and more transparent. But there were times in His youth when there was fear and doubt. Jesus loved nature, and as I understand it, He often went into the wilderness alone to cope with fear and doubt and to pray and commune with His Source. Eventually He found perfect faith and the Divinity within Himself.

When you experience negative emotions such as hatred, jealousy and fear, you allow more and more room for negativity to enter into your mind and spirit. When you can greet even that negativity with love, you don't give it a foothold.

Love is the strongest force in the universe. Your love is a shield around you that protects you from fear and doubt. Your faith is also such a shield. I ask you to consider the lines of the twenty-third Psalm: "Yea, though I walk through the valley of the shadow of death, I will fear no evil." You are not promised that there will be no evil, but you can learn not to fear evil if you can see whatever negativity surrounds you as not separate from the Divine and offer love to it. In doing that, you cannot be harmed. God alone cannot protect you. You always have free will. It is your love and faith that protect you.

The essence of what Jesus learned as a young man was to move past fixation on fear and doubt. He understood that if He continued the course of His life as He saw He must, there would be great pain. He nurtured His faith to face that pain and to do the work He had come to do. He also faced what any being faces in incarnating as human. Although He was born from beyond any human plane, He knew that if He created any adhering karma for Himself, He would need to incarnate again to deal with that karma.

All beings face the same situation. If there is misunderstanding that leads you into rage or hatred and creates karma, and you do not practice forgiveness but self-identify with those emotions, then you become fixed in the human form and must return – perhaps for many lifetimes – to work your way out of it. This is not punishment. It will just take you time for what you came to learn. And you will emerge stronger and wiser for it; but, as you probably already know, it can be painful.

I would suggest that thinking about Jesus and His life example can be of some comfort in that situation. He too had to try to avoid this entrapment. You would all like to be ready to move on to the next stage of your growth; to experience yourself as bodies of light, beyond the need for physical manifestation. And so, it is the same lesson for all of you: to be aware of where you are creating new karma; to work more and more at compassion and forgiveness of yourself and others.

Until Jesus was able to move past all fear and doubt and establish a level of faith where negativity could not find any chink to enter, He was not able to advance with His work. Thus, it was necessary for Him to become fully comfortable with His humanness, so that even in that form He could give unconditional love.

Life is for learning. No one forces us to do the right thing. Within our being, God has given us several important gifts: free will, the seed of our awareness of Him, and that we can be like Him. Suffering is a result of selfish, unskillful choices we make. Our choices arise out of our free will. These choices, once activated, create consequences. Look around at life on our earth. There is so much suffering; so many negative consequences from our self-centered actions. Because the seed of Divine-awareness is within us, we are indeed capable of making far more skillful choices and, therefore, creating a more positive life for us all.

God is the Source and that same Divinity and ability for Creation are within us. Therefore, through our thoughts, words and actions we too are creators. As we look around at the mess this planet is in, some of us simply want to blame God or draw conclusions that delete ourselves from the equation. We desperately need to have a closer look; to discover the unlimited and Divine resources and potential within ourselves. Then, as our awareness of our participation in the world grows, we can understand our responsibilities as co-creators.

Every religion with a foundation of love is a viable path toward God. Those who do not accept Jesus as a Son of God in the traditional way may still find great love for Him and what He taught. They are then challenged to learn about love and forgiveness without the inspiration that Jesus offered, and that is an even harder task.

Jesus' quote, "No one may come to the Father but through Me," has been widely misinterpreted by those who use it for the power of the church to mean that one must take Christ as one's personal savior in order to move toward God. That is not what He meant at all. His 'through me' was not meant as personal 'through me.' Rather, He meant that the Way is through this knowing of the Divinity of all that is, through a path of forgiveness, acceptance and love, and especially through the living of Christ Consciousness and the revelation of it within ourselves.

Jesus did not come to teach you of His glory, but of yours. When He said, "I am the way," He meant that in understanding His Divinity, we must recognize our own. As we advance in recognition of our own divinity, there comes enormous responsibility. This is why so many people are reluctant to recognize their divinity and their power, and would even deny that that is what Christ meant.

It is the Divinity that He and each of us carry. It would be more accurate to rephrase that statement as, 'No one may come to the truth but through the opening of the personal self to its own deepest truth of non-separation and love.' That is the way for the soul to evolve, and none may go there but through that path, learning the lessons of love as exemplified in the life of Jesus.

This divine personal awareness can be found through others who are highly evolved beings that are capable of guiding you toward God's light and love. It is your choice; recognition of the one who resonates most in your heart. Jesus is one who has mastered the perfection of God. But seeing as how most of us humans fall far short of our own potential, let alone that of Christ, there are still others among us who are farther along than we are and who are quite capable of helping us. It is more the guidance system in our hearts that matters, rather than the specific spiritual being that guides you there.

Some people within the church have distorted the meaning of Christianity. Perhaps murder and ill will have been performed in Christ's name as much as has love, sad though that fact may be. Outside of that tragic reality, there are a great many dedicated Christians who are not members of the church, and who have no interest in being identified with any particular denomination. Yet, they are wholly intent on learning to forgive and love each other, to harm no being; and to learn these lessons that Jesus has taught. In doing that, they most certainly are followers of Christ. It has nothing to do with the Christian church, only that they follow the lessons taught by such a great Master. It is entirely possible to know and love God, to follow God, and to improve one's spiritual awareness without ever having set foot in a church.

For those of you who are members of any specific religious organization, I ask you, if the founder of your religion came back to earth today, would your church or temple welcome that one, or would that one be labeled a heretic? What are we creating in the name of love? How are we dividing ourselves so that one religion conflicts with another in the name of righteousness? Perhaps we are coming to a time on earth when our labels do more harm than good. There is not necessarily harm in following religious doctrine, but it is useful to ask yourself, "Why do I need to label myself? Does that label separate me from others? Do I judge myself to be better than them? Am I a part of the solution that pulls all beings together; or am I a part of the problem that creates and promotes separation"?

Jesus' life and His death spoke not only to those who were alive during His time on earth, but to each succeeding generation. Thus the message of His life may have spoken to each of you many times in different incarnations. Those of you who have lived in darkness in the past are slowly learning the lessons of love. At the time when you are ready to hear this message, then you will be moved by it, touched by it and will live increasingly skillful lives. Each of you is in the on-going process of growing away from service to self and toward service to others.

On another subject, Jesus did practice meditation and had met practitioners of Buddhism. From the

Buddhist perspective, Jesus would be thought of as a Bodhisattva: a Being who is already fully realized; fully aware of all He has ever been. In His presence as Christ, He needed a way to bring forth the teachings of heaven and reveal them through His humanness on earth. It would have been very easy to fall into the trap of preaching rather than actually living His truth. And of course, had He not lived it one hundred percent, it would have lost its authority.

Jesus came into the world specifically because so many beings could not grasp the message of compassion and of the Divinity of all-that-is. They were caught up in their own ancient teachings of fear; a darkness of their own making. They needed a door that opened to forgiveness. Jesus was that door. Just to be in His presence, even in silence, was a profound teaching. Even more, the way He was with people, how He carried Himself, and the quality of His actions and speech were also profound. Any person who aspired to loving kindness could not come into His presence without feeling His Light and opening their hearts to Him.

It is with joy that I offer these stories, with the hope that they help you to find the Inner Christ.

Stories of Jesus

One

At the time of the birth of Jesus I was a young boy, five years old. I was a shepherd near the town of Bethlehem, dwelling in the hills with my father and older brother. I was old enough to accompany them for one of my first late evenings outdoors. It was a very peaceful scene that night. I sat wrapped in a blanket by the fire. My father and the other men told stories. Later, the night grew very still. In the near distance, there was a very brilliant star. We all saw it. Below us in the valley, some distance away, was Bethlehem.

Never had I seen a star like that before, nor, I would assume, had the elders because they all grew quiet. As it grew brighter, some felt afraid, but most felt a deep sense of peace and wonder. You have seen how a full moon shines on a snowy place, the way everything seems lit up. That star did the same thing. The whole scene seemed lit in the distance. There was such a sense of deep peace; such a brilliance to the light. And music seemed to fill the air; not heard with our ears, but with our hearts.

Through all the lives I have lived, including the time spent in-between life times; it has been enough for me, just to remember the love and the wonder of that moment. It seemed that a doorway between heaven and earth had briefly opened, and that some of heaven was pouring through to the earth.

We were drawn as if by a magnet, to descend the hills and approach the town. My father was hesitant to go too far from our sheep so we did not go all the way, but stood on a hill perhaps a mile away. It was a night unlike any I have ever known, before or since. The air was filled with angelic presences, which in itself is not unusual; the air is often filled with loving spirits. What was unusual was the strength of this Being Who was coming through to earth. Even those who would have been skeptical of the existence of such a Being could sense the strength of the Energy that was present; and the Love radiating. And so, many were in awe of this Being; having some sense that this was someone special. My strongest memory is one of deep peace and a profound joy, that something had happened far beyond the understanding of the young boy that I was; something that would profoundly change the world.

Many went all the way to town. Others of us stayed closer to our flocks on the hillside. But no matter where you were, this light permeated everything. I cannot say it came from just that star. It seemed almost as if the earth itself glowed. We were in awe. Many of the adults began to pray.

We sat there for many hours. Some of those who had gone all the way to town began to return. I was dozing by this time but I still heard the faint words of elders near me in the still of the early morning hours: "A child is born. They call Him the Prince of Peace. They say that His teachings will change the world." And then I remember that my father's strong arms lifted me up and carried me back up the hill to our fire. I slept with a sense of joy and peace as I had never known before and rarely since; a sense that somehow much that had been wrong with the world was going to be righted, that new hope was offered to the world.

Although they did not see each other very often, my father and Joseph and Mary were friends and brothers in the spiritual community. The next day I had the opportunity to walk with my father to see the baby Jesus. We brought Him an orphaned lamb as a gift. This visit was a great blessing to me. I was given the opportunity to hold the blessed infant and there was such deep joy in His presence. I could feel from Him a sense of love and profound peace. He did not cry in the way many newborns cry. I'm sure that when He was hungry or uncomfortable He gave voice to His needs. But mostly He simply radiated peace, and He met my eyes with a deep loving focus.

And then – you know His history – His family took Him away for reasons of safety and I did not see Him again for a number of years.

Two

When I first saw Jesus, even as the newborn infant, I became totally devoted to Him. I knew that this was a person Whom I would follow anywhere. He simply radiated peace and love. And yet, He did not make use of that for His own power. This was one of the most essential things about Him. I know that stories are told of miracles that He did; but far more important are the much quieter miracles He performed through the depth of His loving kindness.

The adult Jesus was a magnet for children. When children were near He was rarely without them by His side. He truly knew how to talk to children, because He saw divinity in each of them and He invited it forth in a joyful and loving way. He would get down on the ground and wrestle lovingly and playfully with the boys. He knew how to bring a laugh of delight from little girls.

Sometimes children became a bit rowdy, but Jesus' energy was such that a simple hush sound from Him quieted them down. Never did He resort to shaming somebody. If a child was overly boisterous He would hug them into quietness, never speaking down to them.

Although I was five years older than Him, later in my childhood Jesus and I became close friends.

When we were young, Jesus accompanied me on a trip into the hills. I was used to being there alone while tending my sheep. His parents allowed him to join me for a few days. As we walked, we passed some children beating a dog. Jesus became so angry at them that He said He felt like He wanted to hit them back. I knew these boys and I was bigger and older than them, so they left the dog alone and it ran off. Jesus and I walked a ways past them and then we sat down together. In a few moments I could see Jesus release His anger. I watched Him in awe as He transformed Himself, and within a few minutes He became peaceful. I asked Him, "Where did the anger go?" This marvelous young child's reply was, "Love took it."

In this way Jesus was teaching me that we do not have to self-identify with the darkness and negativity that come upon us. And we do not have to be afraid or feel ashamed when these feelings do arise, as they likely will when the conditions are present. We can let love flow through our hearts and it will release the feelings. If they don't release quickly, that is okay too. They will release when they release; we are not trying to push them away. Rather, we are focusing on the predominance and power of love; not giving excessive attention to negative expression.

Three

Another time, when I was twelve, there was a young boy my age who lived in our village. He had a hunched back and walked with a limp and his mind was not clear. He had the understanding of a three-year-old. He could only follow simple directions. He sometimes drooled a bit and children frequently teased him.

I remember the first time that young Jesus met this boy. We had been at my father's house in the village and were going up in the hills to tend the sheep for several days. As we walked down the street this boy came out of his house and waved at us. There was a gang of bullies nearby, as there often are within groups of children. They saw him waving and they began to mock him, imitating him in a cruel way.

Young Jesus walked up to the hunch-backed child and took his hand. He asked me, "May he come with us?" and I said yes. Other times this boy had come with me to the hills for a few hours. I knew that if he came with me I would need to bring him back, as he could not be left alone; but his parents trusted me with him. His mother was nearby and nodded her consent.

So Jesus, meeting him for the first time, simply took his hand and brought him along with us. This boy did not have much understanding and during our walk we came upon an injured small animal. The boy moved to kick it and Jesus put his hand on the boy's arm. Remember, we're talking about Jesus as a child here.

The boy was big for his age, even with his humped-over back.

"No," Jesus said, and He picked up the small animal and put it in the boy's arms and showed him how to hold it and pat it. The boy held the creature all afternoon, tending to it, loving it. Jesus occasionally held it as well then returned it to the boy.

The boy was changed after that. When he had come with me before, I had seen a streak of cruelty in him. He was probably mirroring the cruelty he had received from other children. But watching this young Jesus holding the injured animal and offering it love, the boy suddenly became radiant. He learned how to express that loving heart within himself. No matter that he was feeble-minded and his body carried distortion, he still found that deep healing in himself to know he was capable of love; that he was love. And this is what Jesus came to teach to us all.

In His youth sometimes Jesus would get angry. He worked hard to learn how to be present with His anger, not to condemn Himself for it. But He learned it well, and quickly. Also, in order for Jesus to come into His Divine maturity, He learned how to be present with fear, anger and confusion. He had to learn to express His human-ness and not use it for harm in the world, or be controlled by it. He knew that life would ask of Him to be present in situations in which there would be much catalyst for anger, fear, and confusion. So He learned to hold space for them.

Four

Around the same age, some of us were practicing with a slingshot, hitting our rocks against a post. Jesus was perhaps the youngest among us. He drew the sling back and let it go. The rock missed the post, and then we heard a squawking noise and then a cry as the rock went into the brush beyond the post. He went to look and saw that His rock had accidentally hit a bird that was nesting there. He was broken-hearted. He picked this creature up in His hands and held it. It was bleeding a bit. The stone had hit its side.

A feeling of shame and despair arose in Him. He began to shake and become angry and blame Himself. But He quickly realized His anger. And then He did the same thing that He had done before. He sat down and said, "This is also anger." And He began to breathe with it while He was trembling and still holding the bird. I watched Jesus calm Himself. His facial expression changed and He began to smile, releasing the shame and self-anger. He held the bird very tenderly for quite a while and then took it to His mother.

Later that day I was told that the bird simply flew off from the container in which they had placed it, seemingly unhurt. I can't help but think that it was because of the power of His love. Because He was able to love Himself, He was able to offer the same love to the bird. If He had maintained anger at Himself for hurting the bird, then He would have also been angry at the bird for being in the line of His stone. He would have needed to blame Himself and the bird.

What Jesus was learning in those early years was how to surrender the ego in order to express the Divine self, which is what He came to share with the world.

Five

Another memory, perhaps a year later: Many of the shepherd boys in the hills would kill snakes because they could injure the sheep and other farm animals. Snakes were thus thought to be bad. Young Jesus and I were in the hills together and came upon some boys with knives striking at a snake.

"What are you doing?" said little Jesus.

"Killing the snake," said one of the boys.

Jesus asked, "Why would you kill a snake?"

And the boy said, "Because it is evil." These boys were older and twice Jesus' size and not afraid to speak out.

Jesus replied, "No creature is evil," and He pushed them aside and reached in and picked up the snake and held it gently. He carried it around for a week, taking care of it until its wounds healed, and then He set it free.

Six

When we were in our early teens, we took several days to climb to the top of a mountain. Three other boys were with us. Jesus was the youngest and I was the oldest. We walked for three days into the wilderness. It was an arduous climb. One of the boys fell and sprained his ankle. It was clear that he could not walk any further. What were we going to do?

As the oldest, I was responsible for all of us. I did not feel I could leave one of the younger ones with the injured boy while the rest of us finished our climb. Yet part of me was saying, "We have to get to the top. This is what we came for." So I was still trying to figure out how we could climb this mountain when Jesus said to me, "It doesn't matter. We will just stop. We do not have to climb the mountain. We can't leave him here alone. We'll just stay here with him."

The boy was too big for me to carry. We had adequate food because we had planned several days' journey back. So we just camped. And as I had assumed, when we did not return on time, people came looking for us. One of those adults was able to carry the boy.

During those three days each of us kept looking at the peak, which was in plain sight, maybe just three-hours distant. Couldn't we still go up? Couldn't we take turns watching the boy? This was the ego: wanting, wanting, wanting. And Jesus was the one who kept saying, "No. Let it go. It doesn't matter."

It was so powerful to watch His focus and assuredness. He learned how to carry on and fulfill the deeper heart's direction.

Seven

We were older now. Jesus was a teenager and I was a young man. This was the last time He came into the hills with me. It began to snow during the night, with a cold wind blowing. We had rounded up the sheep, but one lamb was missing. I said to Him, "One is missing, but it doesn't matter. We must find shelter."

Jesus could not ignore this. He said, "It DOES matter. That lamb will die. I will go look for it."

I said, "I'm worried about you. You could get hurt."

He said, "Yes, I could get hurt; but I will be careful. If I don't go, the lamb will die." We compromised and went together. I herded the animals into a sheltered place, used some rope for a make-shift pen, and then we set off to find the lost lamb.

There was cold sleet, with an icy wind blowing. We couldn't see very far in front of us. We were both wet and shivering. Each time I started to say, "We need to stop," He said, "No. We will find him." Jesus was smaller than me and I would imagine that He was colder than I was, but He did not let that deter Him.

This is all about whether we act from a place of love or a place of fear – the fear dictated by the ego. Simply and clearly, Love told Jesus to find the lamb; which we did. It had fallen into a small crevice and could not get out. Jesus retrieved the lamb and tucked it under His robes, warming it with His body. When we got back to our encampment and the fire, He kept it against His body until it was warm, and then He gently returned it to its mother.

The next morning the sun came out and dried up everything. The lamb was happy and playful. Jesus simply smiled at me as we watched this little lamb play and He said, "It did matter."

Eight

I knew Jesus through His early years and then He grew up and went away. There were many years that I did not see Him. When He came back I reunited with Him whenever I could. He was not yet the perfect teacher that He would soon become, but He was quickly and constantly moving into readiness for that role.

One time Jesus had been traveling near where I was, and that was why I was able to go and see Him. On my way I was stopped by robbers. They took my extra clothing and the shoes from my feet. They left me only with my underclothes and a small amount of water. In that condition I traveled for two more days over rugged terrain. When I finally reached Jesus' encampment, my feet were bleeding and I was very, very thirsty. I suppose He could have touched me and instantly healed my feet, but He did not do that. Instead He sat me down and provided some food and water. And then, with His own hands, He washed my feet and bandaged them. They were so badly cut that it would have easily taken a few weeks or more for them to heal. And yet, in three or four days they were healed. I didn't even wonder about it then. As I look back, I recognize that it was the power of His love that accelerated the healing.

Had He miraculously healed my feet immediately, I would have been in awe of Him, and He did not want that. He did not want blind devotion. It is this quality of Him that perhaps I most cherished. He understood that He was human and also Divine. But He did not want to be worshipped as a god. For a god to teach forgiveness, to teach that one should turn the other cheek and love those who torment others, people could surmise that to be easy for Him to do because He was not human. But the point is that He was fully human. He felt the same pain as any other person. He had the same desire for love as any other person would have. But Jesus, more than any other being in history, clearly understood the depth of His Divine Spirit.

That same divine spirit resides in each of you. Even though you are not fully evolved as He was, nevertheless, your essence is no less holy; and no less perfect and beautiful. This is what was so wonderful about Him: He knew that to be an effective teacher He had to work within His humanness. He let people see that He bled when He was cut. He let people see that He felt pain when there was pain, and that He could still forgive and love unconditionally.

The epitome of His humanness was in His death. Certainly one as powerful as He, could have avoided such a painful death if He had so chosen. What would have happened to all that He taught if He had escaped that death and instead allowed Himself to become a powerful King whom many would idolize? Could His message of love have been any more clearly taught than through those beautiful words as He died in agony, "Forgive them for they know not what they do."

How can we follow that message with our hearts today? The lessons that Jesus taught are truly the challenges of all of our lives: to learn that level of unconditional love, as well as compassion and forgiveness; and to truly have peace in our own hearts so that the infinite power of the Eternal may flow through us, to All That Is.

Nine

During one of the many times I traveled with Jesus, we came to a village where His reputation had preceded Him. Some of the people shunned Him, others sought His love and teachings, and some were indifferent. Those who chose to honor Him did so by serving Him the very best of what food they had; they wanted the offering to be as elaborate as possible. This village was rural and poor. It was obvious that there was a scarcity of food among the residents. We all sat down on the ground to eat, as this was the custom in that time. We were all very hungry from our journey. They served Jesus first with a plate of the best of the foods they had.

In the background was a young child watching. He was thin and appeared to be undernourished. He had sores on his body. One of the hosts noticed Jesus looking at the child, and went to shoo the child away.

"Get out of here; go on!" Then to Jesus the host said, "That is the child of one who disdains you."

Jesus simply stood up with His bowl of food and carried it toward the child. The child was frightened; but in a soft voice Jesus said, "I will not hurt you. Would you like food?" And He sat down right there and handed the bowl to the child. Then He asked for clean cloths and water. While the child ate, Jesus washed his sores.

Just that. There was no lecture to the people watching. Words were totally unnecessary. The simplicity and grace of His gesture were all that was needed. Teaching us how to treat others by His living example, was the hallmark of Jesus' lessons to us. Again and again He would work on the heart of any matter, good or bad, with absolute focus on loving kindness and fairness to all. His healing skills in the realm of human behavior were unprecedented; even perfect. His grace in these matters often dissolved the confusion and critical nature of many observers.

There were other children there. Seeing this one eating, they became a bit bolder. In this manner, food was shared with all. Somehow there was plenty. I don't know if He used Higher powers or how it happened, but there was enough for all to eat who were hungry.

Ten

Whenever word came that Jesus was traveling near to where I lived, I would have the great joy of spending some days with Him. There were many people with Him and I was not one of the chosen or select few in any way.

I remember a day when we were gathered in an old barn seeking shelter from a great storm. The roof was leaking everywhere, but it was still better than no shelter at all. There was a sort of thatch material present with which to mend the roof. The owner of the barn was injured and unable to do the much needed work. So when the rain intermittently let up, some of the younger and stronger of us went out in the cold and rain to repair the roof as best we could. It is a job far easier to do in nice weather.

Although He did not have to, Jesus came with us. He could have stayed in the driest spot and everyone would certainly have accepted that. He didn't talk about helping; He just came. Such work in cold weather caused our hands to become raw and bleeding; especially our finger tips. His hands bled along with ours. I am sure He could have stopped that, had He wanted to. Instead He bore it with all of us. When we were done and came inside He took each of our hands in His, not to perform miracles, but as a way of saying thank you; just of sharing the comradeship. At His touch there was healing. The pain receded almost to the point that we weren't aware of how it began. I am sure that He could have instantly healed our torn hands; He was able to perform such miracles. He chose not to awe us, but rather to do His healing quietly.

What I always responded to most were His love, humility, honesty, and His kindness. To me His greatest gift was to serve – even to that degree – and the fact that although He could have, He did not avoid, in any way, the pain of being human. It is one thing for us to receive Divine guidance, and another thing altogether to see a fellow human being practice what He preaches, even to His own death. The power of that was so profound, and forced itself deeply into my consciousness. Can you see that even the smallest avoidance of that choice to live fully human would have set Him apart so that His teaching could not have been nearly as effective? And He knew that.

Eleven

The year my wife died I was feeling deep grief, for I loved her very much. Hearing that Jesus was just a few days' walk away, I left my younger children with relatives and with my son Mark, went to where Jesus was. While walking on a rocky slope I slipped and fell quite a way down the slope and broke my leg. People came to help. They bound the leg, and as I was not far from where Jesus was camped, they carried me to Him.

This was a man who could perform miracles; Who could heal the blind and raise the paralyzed up on their legs. Jesus usually preferred not to perform such miracles, because He did not want to be worshiped as a god, but rather to be known as a man. He taught that what He could do, we could do also. He understood that it was not my leg that most needed healing, but my heart, which was broken from the loss of my wife. I had small children and I did not know how I would raise them alone. What would I do without my beloved companion?

I beseeched Jesus, "Heal my leg. I must go home to my children and to my sheep." He simply looked at me and said, "Your son Mark can tend the sheep." And it was true that the children were well cared for by loving relatives. It was my fear that was pulling me home, and He understood that I was afraid that if I stayed there with Him my heart would break, because somehow, just being in His presence would pull out the grief I was holding so tightly inside me.

It took six weeks for my leg to heal. For the first two weeks I was very angry with Jesus. I was helpless. I could not walk; only be carried. He saw that I was well tended, but I pushed Him aside. Why would He not heal my leg? I knew He could. But slowly my heart began to soften, and I understood that I was not there for my leg, but for the healing of my heart. His love helped me to let go of my wife, and to once again trust my life. By the time my leg was healed, I was ready to go back into the hills to my family and sheep; with a confidence and faith that everything would be just as it needed to be. That is when I learned the lesson: 'Thy will be done.'

My anger did not threaten or upset Him. It's not that He found my feelings to be trivial. Simply, He was not afraid of my anger. If I would not speak to Him because He would not heal my leg, that was fine. He knew what I needed, which I did not then know. I would have rushed back to the hills filled with the same fear and anguish with which I had left them.

I am only one thread in the tapestry of life. May I make a thread as beautiful and radiant as possible. Thy will be done. I then thought: May Your love and generosity shine brilliantly on all of our lives; even unto death. I will trust Your plan.

Even now I hear His words, "Lift this burden from me; but if it be Thy will, I will carry it."

Twelve

Jesus usually did not eat meat. It was not a strictly maintained doctrine of vegetarianism; He simply preferred not to eat meat. But also, out of courtesy, when He was a guest for a meal, He gratefully ate that which was given. Of those who knew Him, very few ever served meat.

One day I was with Him in a small group. We had been walking all day in the rain and we were quite wet, tired and hungry. All we had eaten all day was a bit of warmed grain early that morning. We came to a place where it seemed that we might rest. There was a cave, of sorts, to provide adequate shelter. But we had no food with us.

Soon a young boy appeared and we spoke to him, asking, "Do you know where we can find food?"

And the boy said proudly, "I'll get you food." He was back in about an hour with his arms full of small animals that he had just killed.

Some of us ate meat more readily than others, but we all knew Jesus' preference not to. The child felt so proud for having provided for us. I remember how lovingly Jesus knelt down and received that gift, asked us to clean and cook it, and invited the boy to sit and eat with us. There was such a generosity of spirit. As we were cooking the meat a family came by. They had bread and some vegetables with them and Jesus invited them to stay and eat with us. We ended up having a full and balanced meal.

Before we began to eat, Jesus spoke very movingly of the life force in the wheat, vegetables and animals. He asked us to be aware that the food and we people were all a part of life, and not separate one from another. He reminded us that the human cannot exist without nourishment, which we must draw from other forms of life. He asked that we consecrate that gift as we took it into our bodies; that it would nourish us so that we may serve others, and that they, in turn, would serve even others.

Thirteen

Much of the time Jesus spoke very simply, if at all. Much of His teaching was in deeds and not in words. When He did speak people would hear His words at the level that they were ready to hear, as with the reading of these words right now. Those who were able to take it deeper could do so. For those who took it on a surface level, that is what they needed at that point.

Never did I hear Him lecture. He did not teach by sitting down with people and telling them, 'Now you should do this and this,' and philosophizing about it. He simply acted in a kind and thorough manner. Although He may have had access to infinite power, He chose not to use it.

On one occasion when I was walking with Jesus and a group of people, we came upon a sheep that was obviously having great difficulty giving birth. She was suffering and there was no caretaker present. Jesus immediately went to look closer to see what could be done. There was a foot sticking out. He could have fixed it in a moment, but instead turned to me and said, "Can you help it?" As a shepherd, I knew just what to do. I was able to insert my hand and push one leg back and pull forth the other. I then twisted and turned the body into the correct position for normal delivery and pulled the lamb out. I wondered as I did it, why did He ask me when He had such power. He said nothing then. We dried off the lamb and placed it with its mother and went on our way. That evening He simply said to me, in response to my unasked question, "Always do things in the simplest way. Never show off your power in order to impress."

That is how He lived. One would not have known His power, except that He gave off a radiance of perfect Energy. It was always so easy to feel the presence of God in Him. He did not ask people to bow to Him or worship Him in any way. He never asked for special treatment. He was simple and direct, and He always taught by His actions. We, in our various stages of evolution often aspire in words or language to give example to perfection. Jesus simply lived it. We all have that God-given potential. Jesus had already achieved it. His work was to remind us that we carry the same seeds of perfection, and our responsibility is to live that Love as best we can.

Fourteen

Once when I was with Him we came to a small town. In that market place, apparently a man whose children were starving had just stolen a loaf of bread. The bread merchant and several others, including a law official, had caught him and were debating what to do with him. The bread merchant wanted him to receive the traditional punishment; to immediately have his hand cut off.

The man was weeping, "My children will starve."

And they lectured back to him, "You should have thought of that." But of course he had only stolen because his children were actually starving. The gathering crowd was of mixed sentiment.

Jesus watched the scene for a few minutes then asked us with Him what food we had. We brought out vegetables, bread and other food.

He said to the bread merchant, "Will you take this in payment?"

The merchant looked at Him and said, "But you are a stranger and that will put you without food."

Jesus simply said, "Our needs will be met. Will you take this in payment?" The merchant agreed, for that was far more than what had been stolen. But he also wanted the stolen loaf to be returned.

Then Jesus said, "No. Will you take this food in payment and give this hungry man the stolen loaf?"

The merchant agreed, then asked, "What will you and your group do for food?"

Jesus simply said, "Our needs will be met." At this point several people, strangers to us, each approached individually and invited us to their house to eat. They started vying with each other for the privilege of hosting the radiant and generous stranger, until Jesus said to them, "Will all of you gather your food so that we may eat together?" This was not a rich village, but over time they had been storing food in case of difficult times. Suddenly people were eager to give and they began to bring what they had. Those who had nothing to contribute stood at the edge of the circle until Jesus invited them, saying, "Sit and eat. Have faith. There will be enough food." And, of course, there was.

It was not through a miracle that Jesus created plenty, although He did occasionally do such things for His own good reasons. In this particular situation Jesus knew that the lesson would be for all of us there to open our hearts and trust. The food was there; it had always been there. He simply asked those who had more to open their hearts and share. But He did not do that by shaming or lecturing them, rather by awakening them to His love, which enabled them to open the eyes of their hearts to the needs of others. A very natural flow. There was no judgment in it; no 'you should give.'

Many months later when we came back through that village, there was no longer any starvation. The villagers had learned to support one another through adequate work and sharing so that everyone there was fed.

So, it was not just the passing moment that He changed. Those who had been afraid had learned to release their fear. This is a true and living example of how to create heaven on earth and good will among men.

Fifteen

Another time a similar situation occurred with some fishermen. Somehow their nets had gotten tangled in such a way that caused everyone's catch to end up in one group's net. When they untangled the mess, they chose to keep all the fish for themselves and returned to the others, their now-empty nets. It was obvious to everyone there what they had done. Their fear and greed made them cling to their fortune. 'Never mind your hunger,' they were thinking. 'Aren't we lucky we've got all the fish.' This was not a culture where they took their fish to market and sold them. There were only so many fish these greedy men could use. Yes, they could have preserved them, but they were closing their hearts to the other's hunger.

As Jesus observed the situation, He did not lecture. He only said, "I see that you have many fish to eat. We have vegetables and bread. Shall we eat together?" He pulled out such abundance that they agreed. To those who had lost their fish He said quietly, "Wait. Be patient." There were some in that group who knew and trusted Jesus; but there was still anger and fear on both sides.

We sat down to eat. Those who had lost their fish stood behind at some distance. One of the group with fish made as if to chase them off but Jesus said, "They do no harm." Those with the many fish began to eat, but those of us who came with Jesus did not. We just sat with our empty plates in front of us, following His lead. They ate of their fish, as well as our vegetables and bread and fruit.

One man looked up and said, "Why aren't you eating?" Jesus said, "No hurry."

How much can a man eat when he is surrounded by hungry people with no food before he finally becomes aware of his own greed and fear? Their leader leaped up and said, "You are taunting us!"

And Jesus said, "No, it is your own fear that is taunting you."

And that person understood and he looked around at all the food and then said to the others, "I am sorry. Will you eat with us?" And of course, again, there was plenty. And again, Jesus knew the way to open the hearts of others. His acts of goodness always set the immediate example of how we should live. Many of those who witnessed Jesus in action learned and grew and spread their loving kindness to others as they continued to move through the events of their lives.

Those who had taken what did not belong to them were offered the non-judgmental opportunity to look at the roots of their own fear and greed and then allow the natural outpouring of their own love and generosity. This was not lectured to them with some moral doctrine, but through Jesus' example they were offered the opportunity to find that love and generosity in their own hearts. His way was to connect each person with their own special beauty; to find their own divinity.

Sixteen

Jesus did not talk much about prayer. He meditated in silence at times and He also prayed with words, but rarely did He lead an organized prayer or ritual. At times when He was in the temples, He participated in ritual prayer because that was the protocol. But He understood that prayer must come from your heart. Reciting words by rote closes the heart and causes one to feel prideful of their religion, and to consider that they may be better than others.

There was a time when some wealthy temple-goers felt that Jesus was disrupting their service. They felt uncomfortably challenged by His method of teaching.

They handed Him a prayer book and asked Him, "How do you pray?" He put the book aside, stood with His head bowed and simply was silent. After a few minutes they asked Him, "Are you going to pray?"

He looked up and said, "Yes, I am praying." It was commonly understood to not interrupt the one leading in prayer.

They waited a few minutes more and said, "Are you going to lead us in prayer?"

He said, "I am leading you in prayer." And again He was silent. Finally some of them began to catch on. So they stood there in silence for five or ten minutes until He spoke the proper closing to the prayer, then thanked them and left.

I do not know how many times He did that. I was with Him that once. I am sure He did it repeatedly. He challenged people where they were, and in that which they were presently doing. He did not throw ideas at them; He just said, "I am praying." Always His heart was filled with love. I think He was able to teach as He did and not lecture because there was no lecture in Him. His heart was so deeply filled with compassion and free of judgment, that He simply shared where and what He was with those around Him; meeting each person exactly where they were.

If a well educated man wanted to talk ideas and philosophy with Jesus that was okay. He would indulge in that intellectual banter for some time and then ask a very simple question like, "Well, where is this taking us? Is this entertaining you? Are you trying to dissuade Me from My philosophy?" And such a one would see that there was no way to dissuade Jesus because He had not come to His philosophy by way of intellect; but rather by a deep, inward knowing. The power of this inner knowing would shatter the intellectual games of His challenger, while also revealing to Him more purity in His heart.

Seventeen

I once saw Jesus with a simple teenage boy who lacked understanding. The boy was walking with a mule that was staggering under the weight of its load. The youth was hitting it repeatedly with a stick. Again, no lecture. Jesus simply walked up to him and said, "Your beast seems to be having difficulty. Are you going to town?"

"Yeah," the boy said.

"Let us help you," said Jesus. And He distributed all the bundles among us so that the mule had nothing left to carry.

The young man watched with some distrust. Jesus then took His own parcel, handed it to another and turned back to the mule. He gently took that animal and, with His arm around it, helped it to walk. And thus, we went into town. And there He washed the beast's cuts, saw that it was fed, all the while speaking to this young man with loving friendship, inquiring about his work. Where was he going? What was his name? Who was his family? What are the things he enjoyed doing?

We left the young man with all his parcels, and his mule comfortably fed and bedded. The boy now had a deeper understanding of love which came to him by actually being loved. Just that. Love one another. Don't talk about it. Do it!

I feel deeply blessed that Jesus was my teacher.

Eighteen

The Christ level is the pure and perfect Body of Light. This is the highest level of being, where personal and universal are joined as one. Christ Awareness is pure Mind; pure Spirit; pure Awareness. It knows everything as perfection. It sees the divine nature within any human. Jesus related to each of us as if we were Divine.

One day I joined Jesus and others as they were traveling. We had some packs carried by a beast of burden. In one pack there were beautiful ceremonial candlesticks. Jesus did observe some forms of Judaism, the religion into which He was born. He did commemorate the Sabbath.

A man joined us and walked with us for two days, keeping to the rear. He was clad in ragged robes, unkempt of appearance and made no eye contact with any of us. On Friday afternoon we noticed that he had disappeared, and we assumed that he had gone on his own way. At sunset the time came to light the Sabbath candles and say prayers. Jesus did not seek out a temple to say His prayers. He felt the earth to be His temple and was content to offer His prayers wherever the sunset found Him. When the pack was opened the candlesticks were missing. Some among us were upset and angry and pointed a finger of blame.

"That wretched one must have taken them. Let us go after him!"

"No," replied Jesus. Then He took the remaining candles and made a small hole in the ground and said, "The earth will serve to hold our candles." He simply inserted the candles into a hole. The prayers were said; the Sabbath was observed.

Soon after that some new candlesticks were given to us by someone along the way and they were again stored in the pack. Less than a week later this same man joined us again. There was no proof that he had stolen the candlesticks, but many among us felt certain that it must have been him. Even though they knew that Jesus had taught forgiveness, they still wanted to accuse him.

This is not a simple story of forgiveness. It goes deeper. To forgive another, there must be something to forgive. At the lowest level of awareness one is not yet awake and will blame others. Such a person does not yet know how to forgive. In the middle level of awareness, one may see the divine in another, but will also see the human thief. One at this level knows to forgive. At the highest level of awareness, one asks, 'was anything stolen?' One at this level knows the soul is not evil; the soul is not the thief. In His compassion He may reach to the human level and offer forgiveness if that human seeks it. And he may speak of the theft at that human level, but without rancor. But such an elevated one knows that forgiveness is not necessary. For one with pure compassion there has been no wrong done. There is nothing to forgive. Jesus always lived on this level.

The men gathered and asked, "What should we do? Shall we confront him?" Jesus knew our thinking.

He walked up to us and simply said, "Let him be. Offer him your love. Let him be." Jesus did not see a thief. This was not what I would consider enabling behavior on Jesus' part. Rather, He related to the highest potential within this man. By doing so, He allowed this man to elevate himself to that highest potential of himself. Jesus welcomed him back and said, "We're glad you were on time to join us again. I hope you can stay with us for the Sabbath this week. Let us walk together."

Late that night this man went to the packs, perhaps thinking, 'I got away with it once; I could do it again.'

He removed the candlesticks, at which point Jesus arose and went to him and said, "You need not do this furtively in the dark. If you have need, take what you need. Is there anything else you need from this pack; anything we can give you?" Never had this man experienced another who trusted him; who invited him to be the best that he could be instead of the worst.

The man began to cry and handed the candlesticks back, saying, "I have need of nothing except your forgiveness."

Jesus said, "There is nothing to forgive," and embraced him.

When I awoke the next morning the men were preparing breakfast, including the thief. But there was a remarkable change in him. He looked at me and smiled! He met my direct gaze. He had begun to grow into his divine self; to manifest his own divinity. He had no more need for the fear that led him to steal, because he had begun to trust the deepest truth of who he was. He became a follower of Jesus and left his thievery behind.

Jesus talked to us about this event that changed one man's life. He taught that anger and greed come from a place of fear within us, which is to be met with compassion and loving kindness. He taught that the root of compassion and forgiveness is understanding. He did not say, 'Forgive with a sense of obligation or duty,' but rather, 'Forgive out of the depths of your own understanding.' For Jesus, forgiveness was a natural conclusion that resulted from loving kindness. He always looked deeply into our true natures and taught us, by way of His example, to do the same for each other. We were not able to see as deeply and clearly as Christ sees, but He did teach us to see the divinity in each situation and each person. This always inspired us to live more skillfully in dealing with ourselves and with others.

Because Jesus so completely forgave, He was sometimes portrayed as naïve as to the evils of the world. He was in no way naïve. He merely saw deeper – past the fear, greed and anger – into the divine perfection of each person's heart. He encouraged each of us to live that divine perfection in ourselves, and to begin to see that in others as well.

Much of His healing and the miracles that He is quoted as having performed came from His ability to see that which is perfect and Divine in the person, regardless of what that person may be exhibiting on the outside. The broken skin of a leper is only the surface appearance. If one sees and believes only that surface appearance, they then go to work to fix the brokenness. Jesus saw inside to the perfect light body of that leper. The strength of His perception was such that He awoke that awareness in the one with the disease. And, just as the thief no longer needed to hold fear that led to his stealing, the leper no longer needed to carry his distorted outward manifestation. Jesus did not heal them. He offered them a choice: "You can dwell in the illusion that the mind or body is distorted and continue to manifest that illusion, or you can come with me into the ever-perfect."

I did not often see Him perform such miracles. His preference was to keep it as simple as possible. When He deemed it necessary He was not beyond offering it, but it was not a miracle. It had a logical, almost scientific basis. Jesus gave humans an option. He awoke them to the fact that this choice was actually theirs, and offered the energy to help lead them into their more skillful choice. If anything is to be considered miraculous, it was His loving perfection and immensely pure Energy incarnate in a human body on planet earth.

Nineteen

But occasionally there were what you would call miracles. One night when I was alone while tending my sheep in the hills, I made the rounds before retiring and discovered that a ewe, close to her time of giving birth, had disappeared. Leaving the rest of my flock in the care of my friends and my son, I went back into the hills in search of the ewe. I was able to see enough by the light of the moon. As I went further into the hills, the wind blew cold. We had come over a pass earlier that day, and I realized that I must have lost her then. She must have stopped, feeling the beginnings of her birth pangs, and I had not noticed. I felt responsible, and also concerned regarding what suffering she might be undergoing alone there.

As I neared the top of the pass, I heard her voice: a sheep's soft, bleating cry. She was indeed giving birth, but it was troublesome, as the lamb was twisted the wrong way. She could not help herself and her straining only jammed the infant tighter. It was an easy matter for me to reach in with my arm and straighten it out and so I twisted this almost-born creature and allowed him to emerge. As I did so, clouds moved in and darkened the night. There I was with an exhausted ewe, and newborn lamb and only the light robe I had wrapped around me to walk. No fire. No protection. The clouds were low, with heavy fog covering the mountainside. All about me were cliffs and ravines. It was not safe to go any further.

I sat down holding the sheep, finding some warmth from her body. I wrapped the baby lamb in my cloak, holding it close to its mother and offering them both some protection. The cloak was not big enough to shelter the three of us. My body began to tremble and my teeth began to chatter. I do not recall consciously praying for help. I recall only that my concern was not only for myself; but also for the ewe and the lamb. Perhaps I did ask that they might not suffer.

I was dozing with the animals and shivering violently when I was suddenly awakened by a strong Light. I looked up and there was Jesus! I could not explain this to myself at that time. I knew that He was not physically present, but nonetheless He was truly there. The Light that came from His body was so brilliant that it pierced the fog. The ewe was able to walk. I picked up the lamb and began to follow this Lighted figure ahead of me. One step at a time, we proceeded over the rocky pass and down the mountain. The fog stopped at a certain level, and below me I saw the valley and the fires of our camp. I turned to thank Him, but He was gone. And so, we descended safely to the fire.

How did this happen? I did not even try to figure it out. I simply gave thanks. Perhaps this could be an example of a miracle; that the Energy body of Jesus knew I was in trouble and came to help me out. That is one way of looking at it, but also somewhat distorted. The Energy of Jesus, and of all great Masters, is always available to you. Each of you has one or more great

Masters who serve as the primary teacher to you, and in whose energy field you most resonate. When you send out a prayer, or even an original, half-conscious request for help, it invites the Energy of that Master. Whether that Being is dead or alive; in this life here, or beyond, does not matter. Jesus is just as available to you today as He was to me that night.

From my present perspective, it is verified that He did not physically come there; although I have no doubt that He was capable of that. Rather, His Thought Energy touched my own highest level of being, and His Light was drawn to me. We are all divine. We can manifest that divinity in varied and remarkable ways. You know stories of people who perform seemingly impossible deeds, such as lifting a car off an injured person. You cannot do that on your own. As a finite being you do not have such power. But when you are connected with the Divine, you are infinite. What the Master does is connect you to the highest level of your own being and allow you to begin to manifest what you need from that level.

Because my primary concern was with the other creatures and not myself, that selflessness opened me to the divinity of my own being, which is truly selfless. Only at that level of being could I have perceived Jesus. Just as with the story of the thief, He invited me to move into the deepest level of myself so that I could see His light and follow it to safety.

Certainly I felt fear that night, but I chose not to act on it. If I did so, that would have been to kill the sheep, take its skin and wrap it around me. I still may have perished. You need not be motivated by fear. When you find deep compassion for your situation and your heart is open, you come into touch with the highest level of your self, which resonates with the highest level of your personal Master. In Jesus, the highest level is ever-present; it is His constant state of being.

It would not have been wrong to kill the sheep and take its skin. But it would have been wrong to do that in fear. The combined wisdom of my Higher Self and the teachings of Jesus, could have been to kill the sheep; and then to offer thanks that it gave its life to help preserve my life. The lesson is not about taking or protecting the life of the sheep; it is about acting in love rather than fear.

When you relate to the highest in another is when you most closely emulate Jesus and also act from that highest level in your self; your own Christ consciousness. Thus you invite the highest level within your self and also invite the highest level within the other. The other may or may not be able to respond to that invitation. Even if he remains a thief, your challenge is to maintain that highest level in your self. Keep the door open to that highest level, even for it to emerge in the heart of the other when he is ready. If you focus on the negative, you slam the door to your greatest potential.

Twenty

Jesus taught us to love one another and also to learn forgiveness. Essential to His teachings are the words, 'Blessed is the peacemaker.' What does it mean to be a peacemaker? Depending on the circumstances, there are variations on this skill, and Jesus was perfectly wise with all of them. To simply watch Him in action with others, was a profound lesson in love, and in holding skillful human relationships. He did get angry at times. He was human. There were times when I heard anger reflected in His voice in response to a situation. He was not afraid of His anger. He did not use it from a place of ego or self-empowerment, or to be in control, or even to be safe. He used it as Energy when He felt it was appropriate, out of concern for the harm that was being done.

One time I was with Him and many others in a village. We were resting in the shade during the hot part of the day when we heard a repeated squeal of pain and terror. Jesus immediately got up and moved toward the sound, and several of us went with Him. Young boys were tormenting a small cat; literally torturing it. I will never forget the expression on His face. It was a mix of rage, grief and compassion all at the same time.

There was powerful rage that shouted, "NO!" I was staggered. I had never heard Him shout like that. And at the same time, tears were streaming down His face.

The children heard His anger. If that 'NO' was all He had given them, it would have only taught them the forceful authority of another adult. But when they saw His tears, they were moved. He picked up the mutilated cat with such tenderness. He held it close to Him, His hands filling with its blood. I believe He could have saved that creature. But I felt that He asked, in a spiritual language, if it agreed to die in order to teach the children a more meaningful lesson. I am sure that Jesus helped minimize its pain and that it died in peace.

Remember, this was a society where even human life was treated lightly, so people thought even less about cruelty to animals. The sight of this powerful man holding the small, bleeding creature and crying over it touched those children's hearts. If He had just walked up to them without the anger and said, "Don't do that," they would have ignored or mocked Him. He was not afraid of His anger or His power.

There were three children. By the time this creature died, one child was weeping with Jesus. One had his head hanging in shame and I could not see his face, but I presume that he also wept. And the third seemed to hold himself aside in defiance.

It was to this one that Jesus handed the body and said, "Let us go together and bury it." The defiant boy took the small creature and as he held the lifeless form in his hands, you could see a change come over him.

He looked up at Jesus and said, "Please forgive me."

Jesus said to him, as I had often heard him say to others in similar situations, "It is not my forgiveness that you need."

"What do I do," the boy said.

"I don't know yet." said Jesus. "We will see."

So they buried this little creature.

Meanwhile Jesus asked quietly, "Is there any sick animal in the village that needs nursing?" A baby goat was brought to Him. The mother was unable to nurse her baby; it was weak and it needed to be bottle-fed. To these boys He said, "You took life, now give life. Learn how it feels to nurture another." Rarely have I seen children take to a task so seriously. During our remaining days near this village we watched them pass that little goat around. They even slept with it at night and awakened regularly to feed it.

You do not teach love through hatred or only strict discipline, but through love. But love has many voices. Jesus said, "Blessed are the meek." He understood meek to mean one who is humble; not weak, and not obsessed with power. He did not use His power to show off, but He was not afraid of His power when He felt it was necessary to use it.

Twenty-One

Another time, Jesus was traveling with a group of followers; myself included. As the days passed and we went through different villages, some people would join us and others would drop off. Many who joined us were strangers. Most people were drawn to Jesus because they wanted to learn loving kindness, forgiveness and peace. But that did not mean that they had yet mastered the greed and anger in themselves.

One night we sat around several small fires. I was not at the same fire as Jesus. A man with a brusque manner had joined us a few days earlier. He talked very little. Some of us felt uncomfortable with him. The evening was cold. My friend next to me had a blanket that he wrapped around himself.

Suddenly, this newcomer said to my friend, "I want that. Your blanket. I want that. Give it to me now!"

"This is my blanket," my friend said, "If you have need, let us see if we can find a spare blanket for you." Then this man came at him with his knife and stabbed him; not fatally, but certainly painfully, and then grabbed the blanket. He was apparently used to getting away with such behavior, because he did not flee; he just wrapped himself and sat down.

Again I saw that same look on Jesus' face. I have rarely seen such a mix of anger and grief at the same time. It was almost overwhelming. The thief was clearly not discomforted by Jesus' anger.

He just looked at Him and said, "Well now its mine."

How do you teach love to one whose heart is not yet ready to love? How do you most skillfully reprimand such a one? How do you disarm him so that he will not harm others? Jesus approached the man and stood very close to him. We all suddenly felt that Jesus had conveyed a strong and frightful image to him. This is one of the few times I ever saw Jesus use His power. I know what I saw and it was terrifying to me. I saw death and desolation. I saw the end result of hatred on earth. It was enough to make me quake and shudder. That man in darkness screamed, and his eyes seemed to bulge out of his head. He dropped the blanket and fled.

We attended to the wounded one, and Jesus' touch helped heal the wounds. We all sat still for a while and then Jesus said, "I will need to go alone now and find him." It was dark and the ground was rocky and barren. He knew that the man could not have gone far. I suppose some inner sense led Jesus there. I do not know what transpired, only that several hours later Jesus came back with that man following him. He would not approach us or our fire, but he did lie down. A blanket was found for him, and he slept.

A few days had gone by when the man asked forgiveness of the one he had stabbed.

My friend said, "Yes, I forgive you."

Later that day when we were gathered by our fire, he came to Jesus and asked, "Will you forgive me?"

Again, those words: "It is not My forgiveness that you need."

"Then whose?" the man asked pitifully, now weeping with his face contorted in emotional pain. He said to Jesus, "If you cannot forgive me, then how can I ask God to forgive me?"

Jesus replied, "You must begin by forgiving yourself."

Jesus was able to direct each person past their greed, anger and fear; and enable them to see into the depths of their own loving hearts. This was such a profound lesson. We must learn to forgive ourselves. Only then can we connect with the Divine in ourselves and begin to live from that Divinity. If you seek forgiveness from others without forgiving yourself, you are refusing to look at the knowledge of your inner perfection. You must ask forgiveness from others, but first you must forgive yourself.

I began to understand how this was the prerequisite for truly creating peace. Jesus' words, 'Love one another' are meaningless unless you can connect with that love in your very own heart. The children who killed the cat were out of touch with that love. By giving them a small animal to save; to literally nurture and feed, He connected them with the loving places inside themselves.

When Jesus said to the blanket thief, "You must learn to forgive yourself," the man hurriedly began to gather his things together to leave.

My friend whom he had stabbed, went over to him and said, "Please stay."

"How can you ask me to stay when I have hurt you?"

My friend had long been a follower of Jesus and thus he said, "Your healing and my healing are part of each other. As my wound heals, so does your heart. Let us heal together."

Then Jesus approached and said, "Will you take care of this man you have stabbed? He cannot walk easily; he needs someone to lean on, and to help prepare his food." Always such a beautiful lesson: by nurturing another, we connect with the loving places within ourselves.

Twenty-Two

We were resting in a town when we heard loud voices nearby. Two men began to fight with each other. Each pulled a knife. An angry crowd quickly gathered around them.

No shout of 'No!' this time. Jesus simply stepped into the middle of the fight and placed Himself between them. If we had not been worried for His safety, it would have almost been funny. He moved with them. They were trying to jab each other, but He kept getting in their way.

They began to push Him, saying, "Get out of our way!"

He said to them, "Is your anger toward each other so vague that you can so easily redirect it to Me?" There was quiet. His words further angered one of them and yet stopped the other one cold in His tracks. Two different responses.

The one who stopped just put his knife back and said, "It doesn't matter." The other one continued to push at his former opponent, and at Jesus.

"Why do you push Me?" Jesus asked.

"Because, you are in my way."

"And if I get out of your way, what are you going to do?"

"I will get back at this good-for-nothing man!"

"At what were you angry?" Jesus asked.

"He spoke wrongly about me in front of others."

"And for this you would kill him? And what after you killed him?"

"Then nobody will wrong me in front of others again."

"What did he say about you?"

"He..." and here the man faltered. "...He said I am violent."

Jesus let out a deep sigh from feeling such sadness at our inhumanity to one another. Hearing His sigh, the man began to understand a deeper truth about himself.

That Divine place that Jesus helps you reach for; is always in you. Although you can block it with anger or fear, it is never absolutely cut off from you. But sometimes when there is much confusion, it is very hard to access that place. Jesus was a Master at guiding others into that access. I believe because He saw that Divine light shine brilliantly, even from the angriest and most confused of Beings, that He went straight for that Light. What seemed impossible, becomes possible. Heart to heart. Light to light. This is the way of love, and of peace.

Twenty-Three

One time I was fortunate to catch up with Jesus as He was walking through the countryside between villages. There were only a few people with Him, and I had the special delight of speaking directly with Him for several hours. To have one-on-one conversation with such a Divine human being is the closest thing to having private time with God. Although His words were rich and the message was always perfect, it was enough just to be so close to Him. The Love and Light somehow radiated out of Him and flowed directly into my heart.

Later, near dusk, we came around a bend and heard some kind of skirmish ahead of us. Then we saw seven or eight people with sticks beating a man.

Jesus stopped the one closest to Him and asked, "Why do you beat him?"

That one replied, "He had asked to travel with us and then, from behind our backs, he stole from us." This man then asked us to join them in the beating.

I wondered what Jesus would do. Would He try to intervene? I think that if the victim's life were in danger, He certainly would have.

As it was He simply said, "No, I do not beat another." Then He moved inside the circle of attackers and sat down close to this man's head, and asked us to sit around him as best we could to offer some protection; a human barrier of sorts.

At first there were angry cries, "Get out of the way," and we also received some indirect hits. Jesus did not flinch, and, mirroring Him, we did the same. They grew frustrated, saying, "But he stole from us!"

Jesus said, "Yes, I understand."

"He deserves much worse than a beating!"

Jesus replied, "He should not have stolen, I agree. I wonder what prompted him to steal. Did any of you ask him?"

An angry retort, "I do not talk to thieves."

"Perhaps he had some reason; some pressing need."

"Yes, he had a reason. His reason is that he is warped; that he is bad; that he is a thief!"

Jesus said, "Perhaps he actually is warped in some way. Perhaps he has not been raised and trained to have proper respect and reverence for other people. Will beating him teach him that?" And on went the dialogue, until those who were doing the beating simply walked off. During the disturbance I was afraid they were going to beat me more, and also Jesus. But His loving and graceful demeanor calmed the violent activity. Jesus was just being present, judging neither side.

When they had left, Jesus tended to the beaten one. Some of his wounds were bleeding. We built a fire, had a meal and slept there for the night. When we awoke in the morning the thief was gone, and also our bag that contained our food. Jesus made no comment on the matter. He just said, "Let us walk on." With the injuries, he could not have gotten very far ahead of us, and soon we saw this thief in the distance. We saw that he tried to hurry, but that his body would not sustain him. He finally fell to the road trembling, crying and probably anticipating another beating.

"Why do you steal?" Jesus asked. The man's face contorted with grief and rage.

"Because, all my life people have stolen from me. I have learned that I must take what I need. It will never be given to me."

"Perhaps you have not encountered the right people," said Jesus. "Perhaps your own fear has led you to interact with others who carry an equal amount of fear. Here are our packs. Please take what you need and leave the rest for us."

I was both amazed and filled with joy at what He did; and yet also very skeptical. I thought to myself, one such as this can never learn. Perhaps he needs to be beaten enough to arouse enough fear in him that he will cease his thievery. But of course the choice was not mine.

The thief got up, and shamefully looked at the ground as he handed the stolen food back to Jesus and said, "I don't need anything."

Jesus said, "Of course you do. Have you had breakfast?"

"No," the man said.

"Well, why don't you sit here and eat with us?"

I think he wanted to do that, but he could not; he was too ashamed. He finally took some bread and fruit and, head hanging down, he walked away.

After our meal we walked down the road. We soon came upon a very poor man in rags, sitting under a tree eating bread and fruit.

"Have you need of more?" we asked.

"No,' he said. "A man just gave me this. I have all I need."

He described the man exactly; it was the thief who had left us. I don't know what became of him. But in witnessing such a change of heart in him, I learned a valuable lesson about myself. It was my fear in me that thought the man needed to be beaten. It was that in me which said, 'Will my needs be met?' If he had asked, Jesus would have given him all of our food because He knew our needs could be met. We may not have had regular meals, but we would not have starved to death. How uncomfortable are we willing to become in order to assist another in greater need than ourselves?

Twenty-Four

There was another time when I was with Him when He did give away our entire dinner. We were traveling in a fairly large group. We passed some other families traveling together. They told us that bandits had taken all their food and clothing. Jesus literally took the shirt from His back − His cloak − and wrapped it around a mother who was holding her baby. He did not ask any of us to contribute in any way. We simply acted, and gave them our food. Many of us also gave our clothing. This is the contagiousness of Jesus' Love.

Out of concern for us they said, "No, then you will be cold and hungry."

Jesus said, "No, we will be fine. We will be taken care of. You take this. We do not need it."

Now, of course, I was afraid. It would be cold that night and the next town was a considerable distance away. I was already hungry. But, in trusting Jesus, I gave away my possessions. I think I expected that when these families had moved on, Jesus would somehow create a miracle and provide for us. But He did not do that. We walked a short distance and He pointed to a spot and said, "This looks like a good place to spend the night." We looked at one another. None of us had cloaks or food or anything warm. It was clear to me that Jesus was teaching us that our needs will always be met, that it is safe to experience some discomfort; and that you do not have to be afraid.

Had He not been present that night, I know that I could not have done what I did. In faith I simply settled down by the fire; hungry, cold and thirsty. I slept as best I could, half-naked on the hard ground. We all shivered and took turns fueling the fire. The morning sun warmed us, and a walk of several hours brought us to a village where people knew him and very joyfully offered us food and clothing.

His giving was always spontaneous, simple and joyful. Never did I see Him give in a premeditated way; nor lecture during His talks. When people gathered and were confused, these messages of Love and Truth would pour out of Him. And to each He always gave, just what that one needed.

Twenty-Five

On another occasion, my son, Mark and I were with Him. Again, there were few of us and I had the great joy of spending time talking with Him. Suddenly, in the distance we heard some bells ringing. They were coming from some caves in the nearby hills. In those times, people with leprosy were cast out of their communities and sent to live with other lepers. The disease was much feared because it was contagious. The lepers rang the bells to warn us to stay away. Of course that had the opposite effect on Jesus. They were people in pain. He simply turned on the trail and went up the hill toward them.

The first person behind Jesus followed Him immediately. The second one turned to look at me, and then back at Jesus.

Jesus stopped and said to us, "You may come or wait. I will be back."

How He challenged us so in this way! I was more afraid for my son than myself, to expose him to this dreadful disease. Jesus did not condemn my fear. He said with His glance, 'I know you are afraid. I know this can be contagious. You do not need to come.' His kindness, which acknowledged my fear with no criticism, allowed me to surmount it and I followed along with my son.

I had never seen lepers this closely before. Some of the disfigurements were quite terrible. Jesus immediately asked for water and simply began to wash wounds. He tore His cloak into strips to bind the sores. The first disciple joined Him. After a few minutes, Jesus turned and looked at me and the man next to me, for the two of us had simply stood there watching. Jesus emitted no shame or expectation toward us. In His eyes was so much kindness for our dilemma.

These people had been so abandoned by the world. They were in terrible pain and had so little. I know that I could not have been the first to help, but with enough faith and courage, I could become another instrument through which love flowed. As I watched Jesus for those few minutes, I clearly saw how He was already such an instrument.

The second man followed Him after a few minutes and began to tend to the others, but I still stood to the side with Mark. Soon Jesus paused in His work and looked at me. He knew that I was a shepherd. He said words that went directly to my heart.

He said, "These are my flock, and I must care for their needs."

I do not know if He was telepathic, but with those few words, the thought came into my mind of the time the previous winter when I had literally faced a wolf-like animal to rescue a ewe and her lamb. I had not been afraid because it was my flock and it was what I needed to do.

I knew that if I continued to not assist, Jesus would in no way condemn me, nor would He love me any less. Then it simply became so clear to me: here is a place where love is needed, and, if I can get past my fear, then I may be an instrument of that love. And so I began to work. My son watched us for a few minutes more and then he too joined in to help. At first my heart ached for him; that he might contract the disease, and I almost bade him to stand aside.

Then Jesus said, "Mark, please come and help me," and my fear dissolved.

When we were finished, we shared our meal with them and spent the night there. In the morning we shared breakfast and left them the rest of our food. Just before we left, Jesus paused to check a few of the wounds. He did no miracles there. But through His Touch and Energy, He called forth the other's ability to heal. The process would be slower than a miracle, but the people would become empowered to learn that they were whole and, with a more loving and positive attitude, they could begin to heal themselves.

Twenty-Six

There is another story that moves me deeply and brings tears to my eyes. I had another son, older than Mark, who was unwell since his early childhood. His joints were crippled. I suppose today one might describe it as juvenile rheumatoid arthritis. I loved this young boy, and it brought such pain to my heart to see how difficult life was for him; how painful every movement was.

I never brought him to see Jesus because he could never walk that far. There came a time when this son fell very ill. His body was inflamed with fever. He wept for days for the pain that he experienced. I had no idea where Jesus was; I had not seen Him in almost a year. All through that night of my son's pain, I prayed, "Please come and save this lad. I know You can do that. Restore him to health. Save him."

And then I began to feel this Energy moving. I did not see Jesus in material form, but in my prayer and meditation I felt His Energy and His thoughts. And the thought I received was, 'You can give him permission to come home. You can allow him to leave this life of suffering and not hold on to him.' Then I understood that my son was trying to live on for me, because he knew that was my need. Again, my fear was intense, for I loved my firstborn so deeply. How could I find the courage to give the gift of letting him go?

Through the night he shivered and sweated with his fever. He screamed and cried; literally out of his mind with fever and pain. Toward dawn the fever broke and he looked at me with clarity. I knew then that I had a choice. I knew if I said to him, "You are strong. You will recover," that he would continue to live on in pain for me. Or I could tell him, "You are free to choose to leave. I love you and will support your choice. If you need to leave, it's okay. I love you."

As that realization of choice came to me, I felt Jesus' loving Energy embrace me, and I heard Him saying, "It is safe." And suddenly I knew that it truly was safe for my son and for me. His essence will survive even his death and I will be okay. As if reading my thoughts, my son looked at me with such gratitude in his eyes. I was aware of how much I had held him to this earth. He simply smiled at me, looked deeply into my eyes, and died. He needed to go home. I needed to give him permission to do so; to transcend my fear and reside in love.

With my deepest gratitude, even now two thousand years later, I thank Jesus, who taught me how to give with such love.

Twenty-Seven

Jesus was kindness personified. But He could also become angry. There are two bases for anger. One is fear-based and comes from the ego and its desire to protect and make gains for the self. The other is a love-based anger, which Jesus always used skillfully. Anger is not the correct word for it; rather, it is a profound sadness that gives rise to Energy, as opposed to a dulling sadness that brings despair. It is a compassionate sadness that inspires effective energetic action and does not cast any blame. Nevertheless, it deals directly with the negative distortion in a person and brings it back into balance. With Jesus, even if anger arose He knew He could be patient and did not have to act upon that anger in ways that would be harmful to another. On the basis of that restraint He was able to see the whole situation with compassion.

One day I was with Jesus and perhaps a dozen other men. You all know the story told in the scriptures of Jesus standing near the woman who was about to be stoned, and his words, "Let those among you who are without fault throw the first stone." The story I tell now came before that. We were outside the home of one of His followers. Suddenly there was shouting, screams and anger on the road nearby. Jesus arose abruptly and we all arose with Him. I do not know what the woman had done, but she was on the ground and people were stoning her. She was bleeding and unconscious. A large cut showed that a stone had hit her head.

I don't think I had ever seen an expression like the one Jesus gave at that moment. There was anger and sadness. He did not know this woman or any of the people gathered around her. He simply walked over and said, "Are you finished?" and looked many of them in the eyes. He knelt down to the woman but she was already dead. He sat there and wept silently.

In my naiveté I did not understand His sorrow. I thought He simply wept for her because she was young and beautiful and her life had been cut short in such a violent way. It was not until later that I realized that He wept for all people and their passions, and for the human fear and hatred that caused them to violate others. And I believe He wept for Himself, for although He had come to teach love, He could not prevent human suffering and the acting-out of peoples' fear-based emotions. He understood that He could only begin a process of enhancing peoples' spiritual awareness that would take millennia to fulfill.

Twenty-Eight

Another time I saw Him weep that way, but there was more anger in His response. This was in the village near my home. It was the only time that He came through that village; a very joyous time for me because it gave my entire family the opportunity to be with Him.

There was a teenage boy who was deaf and mute. He was a simple person. Those who knew him knew he had a loving heart, but many made fun of him. As we walked into the village square we became aware of soft crying. Across the square was a small child, dirty and disheveled. She was making signs that she wanted something to eat, pointing to food. I am sorry to say that no one except the teenage boy was paying attention to her. He saw her hunger. He took a piece of fruit from a merchant's stall and walked to the child and handed it to her.

The merchant, who had known this boy most of his life, and knew that he was deaf, yelled, "Stop, thief!" Of course the boy could not hear him and did not stop. When he handed the fruit to the child, her face lit up. The merchants came out of their stalls and, even though they knew the boy, they began to beat him with sticks. By the time we pushed our way through the crowd, this boy had been severely beaten.

Jesus said in a stern voice that I'd not heard before, "DO YOU KNOW WHAT YOU ARE DOING?" The power in His voice stopped everybody short.

They were ashamed of themselves; a dozen or so men attacking a mute teenage boy with no way to defend himself.

One of the attackers spoke up, "It is the law. He stole. He's done it before."

Jesus said in the same commanding voice, "IT IS ALSO THE LAW: LOVE ONE ANOTHER. HE IS YOUR CHILD AND SHE IS YOUR CHILD," His voice was controlled but I could feel the anger in it. And inside that anger, on His face, again the sorrow and compassion; His knowing that they had acted only as they had been taught.

I sensed that Jesus realized His limitations in dealing with people who lived too much in fear and ignorance. Of course He had immense power and could have used it if He wished. But He would not violate another's free will. He understood that they had to learn kindness by themselves; that He could serve as a guide but He could not do it for them. On His face was etched the dilemma: knowing His infinite power and yet the acknowledgement that He could not change the way things were right there, that any changes He made are those that would be seeds that would take fruit in further years and centuries down the road.

He sat down with tears running down His face and held the boy in His arms. He did not speak again. He looked up at the men and I could see that He wanted to speak but He also knew they would not understand. I know that He had miraculous powers and I believe that He could have saved that boy's life. I think He understood that as much as He understood that He himself eventually needed to die, to be crucified as a part of his example to us. This boy was also giving his life in this way as a teacher to others. He saw that the boy's death would have a much more profound effect upon these men than they would experience if He worked a miracle and revived him. He understood the boy was ready to make that offering. So He sat and cradled the boy while we all stood there and watched him die.

The little girl meanwhile had finished her fruit and came over. She was perhaps two years old.

Jesus looked around and asked, "Does anyone know this child?"

They said yes, she was the baby of a couple in the village.

"Where are the parents?"

"The mother died. The father cares for her."

"Where is the father?"

Again I could feel His anger growing. And yet, it was a controlled and compassionate anger, which had the purpose of leading these men to a deeper wisdom and compassion. He asked in a quiet voice, "Would this baby normally be here alone and hungry? Was there none among you except this young man who realized that she was in some kind of difficulty?" It is the only time I heard Him speak in a way to create a sense of shame to people. It was not His anger talking; but He was asking them to reflect more deeply on how they had reacted and killed out of anger and haste with no self-reflection or restraint. Several of them went to the father's house. There they found him lying on the ground with a broken leg. He had fallen off a ladder.

How do we invite another to wake up? A fully enlightened Being such as Jesus had His own perfect methods. He always knew just what others needed. It is not that He did not experience emotion so much as the fact that emotion did not control Him. He understood how emotion arose and then let it pass by. What drove Him is a generosity of spirit; a willingness to give everything of Himself to others. Jesus has demonstrated that with absolute clarity of heart, anger can be a catalyst for compassion and it can lead to clear, direct truth, offered with no intention to harm, but also with no intention to let oneself be damaged by another. And yet Jesus also knew that each being must resolve its own karma. He can only point the way, then step back and allow each of us freedom of choice.

Through the limited years that I knew the adult Jesus, I watched Him evolve a clearer style of teaching. The more time He spent among us, the more skillful He became at understanding human behavior. I watched Him come to understand more deeply what it means to allow others to make their own mistakes. Jesus' approach was not to punish, but always to teach. His anger was useful because He applied it with non-judgment.

In my times spent with Jesus I would notice judgment arise in me. Then I would observe Jesus respond in a deeply compassionate and non-judgmental way, the message of which was always perfectly clear: "You may not pursue this violence to another." He never said, "You're bad." He simply said, "You may not be violent to another. Look at the roots of your anger." And He said it with so much Love and understanding that the one to whom He spoke did not feel threatened, but deeply loved.

After Jesus left our village there was much change. The baby and its father were taken in by a loving family; something that never could have happened before. People would simply have turned their backs. So this was a process of awakening people. The entire village adopted the baby, and she eventually called many of them "Mama" and "Dada." Everywhere she went people hugged her and fed her. After her father's leg healed they continued to live with this large family at their invitation. They had said to the father, "You cannot be away at work and also care for your daughter. Leave her here and we will care for her."

He said. "No. I need her with me. I love her. She is all that is left of her mother, whom I loved."

So they said, "You stay too."

I am not saying that, before Jesus' visit there was no generosity of spirit; but that often such openheartedness was sleeping. His presence awakened it, not only in that situation but wherever He went.

Twenty-Nine

On another occasion there were only three of us traveling with Jesus. We were walking in an arid area. We had water and a small bit of food with us. We also had some cloth that we could use as a shelter from the hot midday sun. In that area at that time of year, too much exposure to the sun could kill a man. There were no dwellings nearby in which to take shelter.

Suddenly, we were attacked by bandits. They did not know who Jesus was. They took our shelter cloth, our cloaks, our food and all but one small jug of water. To leave us completely waterless would be akin to murder. We walked on after they left but it became clear that we had to shelter ourselves from the sun. We literally burrowed under the sand as best we could. We actually managed to sleep a little.

When we awoke it was late afternoon. We were so thirsty that we could barely talk. We knew that we might need to walk through the night to reach a dwelling for some food and water. It would be an arduous walk. We passed what little water we had around and we each took a sip, then we began to walk.

In an hour or so, of all surprises in this harsh terrain, we found a she-goat who had just given birth by a small cluster of shrubs. She must have wandered from a flock and then became lost. Her infant was nudged up close to her and nursing. Miraculously the mother did have milk, but she herself must have suffered terribly from thirst.

Most men in our situation would have killed the goat, drank the blood and eaten its meat, or killed the baby and taken the mother's milk. Jesus looked at the goat and He looked at us. He did not ask us to give the goat our remaining water. He simply looked at the jug and said, "I wish to give it my share of the water." We knew Him well enough to know that He was not pushing us to follow; that He would not think less of us if we did not also give. And we also knew Him well enough to know that He was not promising that we would survive the night without water. Yes, He could have miraculously brought us more water. But the question was not to survive; it was to learn and to have faith. If we could offer this selfless gift, we would express the abundance of the universe. Whether we lived or died was quite secondary. It was clear that what was necessary was to support this life, and there was simply no question in His mind that this is what had to be done.

So we gave the goat all of our water. It revived a bit. One of us carried the kid and another helped the goat to stand. Alternately it walked and we carried it. It was this conviction in Jesus that was so powerful for me; to offer Himself freely in whatever way He could to wherever there was suffering; to hold nothing back and trust God. It was His absolute Love and Faith that spoke so deeply to my own fear. No words He could have said, no lecture He could have offered would have taught me as did His living example. I had to go through the experience to see how it felt to let go of fear.

I knew at some level that if water did not appear, He was not going to save us. That may sound cruel; but the lesson was that it is safe to give everything regardless of the consequences. We were in a situation that asked truly unconditional giving and directly challenged us to reveal and transmute our deepest fear. We knew that we would probably come to a village by morning, but we would be hard-pressed to make it. I don't think Jesus would have asked us to give the water if it had meant certain death for ourselves. But He did not say that. He did not even ask it of us. He just gave us His example and in our hearts we were led to follow.

I cannot sufficiently express my gratitude to the Creator for the opportunity I was given in that lifetime to occasionally walk by the side of Jesus and to learn so much from Him.

True giving is from the heart; not the mind. Investigate yourself as you offer a gift to anyone for any reason. Is it given with true joy and a sense of love for the recipient? Or is it given with some sense of fear, and wondering what you will get back? Always offer yourself love in the presence of any fear that you may have. Work with loving kindness. Acknowledge the desire to be safe within yourself and then you can acknowledge that same desire in others.

There have been many Masters or highly evolved Beings who have so greatly helped others on their way toward God. Jesus was among the greatest and most highly evolved of them all. He truly was a Son of God. We people of earth are blessed beyond the scope of our understanding that He chose to live here among us. Allow this to serve as a reminder that you are not alone in your endeavors to know and express the Divine. You are always loved. Each of you has within you the same Divine essence and potential – however remote that may seem – to also become a master; to offer your own loving energy to those who would follow you or even listen to you. You are all sons and daughters of God.

Thirty

It was always so inspiring to observe Jesus in His relationships with people: the way He carried Himself; His actions and perfect use of language; each word and the tone of His voice; the selfless eloquence with which He spoke; and always the wisdom, love and compassion perfectly blended into each unique circumstance. The Light of God radiated out from Him all the time.

I was a shepherd, and always responsible to my flock and my family. As such, I could never see as much of Jesus as I wished. Since word of His travels spread before Him, whenever He came near I always laid aside my work to spend a few days in His Presence. And occasionally a friend would offer to watch my flock and family for a few weeks so I could joyfully spend more time with Him.

There is a common phrase in today's world, 'Let go and let God.' What does it mean to put ego aside and allow one's self to be a clear channel to receive Divine wisdom? Jesus was an expert in this. Never have I known another who was so able to channel the Essence of God with such grace and clarity. Jesus taught me faith. In some ways this was His greatest gift to me because when I first knew Him I was impatient and had little faith. I tried to plan and control everything, as if I could make the world and my life come out the way I wanted it. Here was a perfect set-up for another lesson from Jesus.

In one of my early travels with Him, when He was still very young, we moved between villages across a stretch of open wilderness with which only I was familiar. I was asked to accept a position of leadership in terms of guiding us through. I knew the danger of those hills. There were wild animals that could harm a man. In the higher elevations the wind blew cold and rain could turn to sleet. Parts of the way were rocky and steep and dangerous at night.

We left the first village early in the morning so as to cross the mountains before dark. But Jesus would not be hurried. Early in the walk we came upon an old woman carrying a heavy load towards her home. She was struggling and walking with some difficulty. Jesus offered to lift her burden from her and she accepted. He carried it Himself and slowed His pace to match hers for perhaps an hour until we saw her safely home.

We paused to rest and have lunch and I urged Him, "We must move on. We are not yet across the mountains." We were high up and the view was beautiful.

Jesus said to me, "Relax. We will get there when we get there."

I was concerned for our safety and chafed at His easy sense of relaxation. "We must move. We must go!" I said.

Jesus said calmly, "Relax."

We came through the pass between two peaks when we heard a cry; something in distress. Of course

Jesus would not let it be. The rest of the group, there were eight of us, stayed on the path while Jesus asked me to accompany Him up the steep, rocky slope. Soon we came to a wild mountain sheep struggling to give birth. He immediately went to comfort it.

I said to Him, "Creatures live and die in these mountains. You must leave it or we will die. We cannot be up here after sunset or we will die."

He regarded me peacefully and said, "Go if you need to, and take any of those who wish to go also. I will be safe."

Of course I could not leave Him. But I was angry because my fear was taking me over. I argued with Him and said repeatedly, "We must go!"

Jesus said, "How can we go? We cannot move a sheep and carry it along as it is giving birth. This cannot be rushed. Relax."

And so we sat there. He himself went back to tell the others what we were doing and some of them climbed up to join us, while the rest found what shelter they could. Because of my shepherding knowledge, I knew how to properly help this creature, whose infant lay incorrectly in the birth canal. But still I was angry.

As we sat and waited for the birth, the evening grew colder, the wind blew harder and sleet began to fall, making the rocks icy.

"Why do you do this?" I said. "We will die!"

His only reply was, "The sheep needs you. If we leave she will die."

He was so clear. There was no ego in Him or threat in His voice. He did not need to save anybody to uphold anyone's image of Him. His single purpose was to be a vehicle for Divine Light; for love and purity.

As the stormy dusk gathered around us, I truly believe He did not know what would happen. There was no control of the future. There was simply faith that whatever happens will be okay. When you are far enough along on your path to God, you cannot turn your back on suffering. Whatever comes, be it life or death, joy or sorrow, it will be okay. I began to realize that not only was I involved in a lesson for physical survival, but spiritual survival as well.

We had little food or warm clothing with us. We had no shelter. The creature finally gave birth. We then realized that the mother's leg was injured. So after the birth Jesus wrapped the lamb and the mother and we carried them down to a more sheltered area where the others had built a fire. We warmed up a bit, but there was very little wood. Clearly we could not keep the fire going all night. Because I knew the danger in those mountains, I was frightened more than the others. Without light, the way down was impossible. In those conditions at that height the night would become very cold and we could not survive it. And without fire, animals would attack; especially drawn by the blood scent of the birth.

As the last of the fire died, the wind broke up the clouds and the full moon began to shine, brilliantly lighting our path. Jesus stood up and said, "Are you ready to continue?" Much to my wonder, there was no difficulty at all. The night was as light as day. We each took turns carrying the sheep. Jesus himself carried the lamb. We came down from the hills into a valley where a shepherd welcomed us into his home and gave us food and shelter. Jesus may or may not have known the moon was going to come out; but more importantly, He simply trusted. To truly and totally trust was more important than the outcome. I learned that what happens will happen. I had done what I needed to do. I could do nothing else, and so I gave myself in trust. Thy will be done.

Jesus had no self-will, and yet He was so strong at heart in all His endeavors, for the Light of the Divine shone through Him. He was not at all a pushover. He knew when to give and when to say no and stand firm. And both the giving and the firmness came from a place of deep love and clarity of wisdom; not from a place of fear.

Thirty-One

I was walking with Him on another occasion with a small group, traveling between villages. We had been warned that there were robbers. Hearing that news, Jesus simply nodded, not expressing any real concern. Just an hour into our journey a large man accosted us. We had no valuables, but he took our cloaks and food. We walked on through an area that was sparsely inhabited. There was no one to offer us food or clothing. We went hungry that day and slept chilly that night.

Early the next day we came to a small village and were given some food and clothing. Again, an hour into our journey the same man appeared. Jesus showed no fear or alarm at all but said to him in a kindly way, "My brother, how may we serve you today?"

He pointed to our feet. "Your sandals." And so we all took off our sandals and gave them to him.

Again we walked on, experiencing considerable discomfort, as the ground was rocky. Late in the day we came to a very small village, and out of some animal skins given to us, we were able to make some kind of footwear. We were given more food and a place to sleep.

The next day we were just about to eat the food the villagers had so kindly given us, when the large man appeared yet again.

"Your food," he said. "Give it to me."

"Of course," said Jesus. "Take what you need."

This robber did not know who Jesus was, but, as I have said, one could not help but see the Light shining out of Him. For those who were too much in darkness to tolerate that Light, it was like a nightmare to them. For others it had tremendous healing power. It was a potent invitation to remember their own divinity. This man gathered our food and began to leave, and then he stopped and turned back.

He said, "There are six of you and one of me. Why have you simply given me what I asked for day after day? Why have you not beaten me or even tried to kill me?"

Jesus simply said to him, "You asked because you had need. Not understanding the nature of your need, you thought you needed our possessions. Now do you understand what it is you really need?"

And the man began to weep, saying, "I have lived my life for so long stealing from others. I want to start anew, but I don't know how. I can never be forgiven for the harm I have done. What I need is forgiveness."

Jesus looked at him and asked, "Can you forgive yourself."

The man wept, "No. I cannot."

Jesus took his hands and said, "I forgive you. Will you walk with us?"

"You really want me to walk with you? I who have stolen from you and abused you?"

"Yes. Will you walk with us?"

And he did. And this man later became a disciple of the Master and a teacher of forgiveness to others. Because of deep insights gained from his own earlier experiences, he was able to touch the hearts of those who had withdrawn into their own fear. Each time we were robbed by him I had wondered why Jesus allowed it. In His infinite wisdom He saw the Light in this being, and that it was accessible. Jesus had no fear. He understood this man's soul and that the things he asked for were a symbol for what he really needed.

And yet in a very similar situation, Jesus' response was quite different. During another time of travel with Him we had come to a village. Two of His disciples who were there had laid out a fine meal for us. As we sat to eat, a man approached on a donkey bearing weapons. And he said, "You will give me that food!"

"No," replied Jesus.

"Do you know that I could kill you?" said the robber.

"Of course you could kill me. Will that resolve your dilemma? How many of us would you kill? And do you really wish to kill?"

Jesus stood up, placing Himself between us and this man. There was no fear-based anger, but there was anger in His words. There was a firmness which clearly implied, 'No. You may not do this.' The two of them looked at each other in silence for nearly a minute and then the robber turned and left. This is a lesson about one's ability to trust deeply what goodness wells up inside Him and to act on the whisperings in His heart.

It seems to me that the greatness of Jesus' faith was such because of His lack of fear, and fear is so difficult for the ordinary person. There was a powerful certainty in His motives; not distracted or weakened by any ego or doubt or lack of faith. And out of that clarity He had the ability to attend to suffering in the most skillful ways, which was simply to be the instrument of Divine Will. The people often wanted miracles from Him. His preferred sort of miracle was simply to use the best of the human heart to act in a purely loving way.

Thirty-Two

Once I was with Jesus in a village where a child was very sick. The father asked Him to come to his hut and heal the child. Jesus came and sat with the child and mother and father through the long night while the child's fever burned. It seemed to me that He took away the child's pain because in the first moments of His presence the child stopped crying and relaxed. How did He know whether to use His healing power, or let the natural events unfold? By morning the child had died. The parents grieved, and were also angry.

"Why did you not save him?" they asked.

Jesus would not answer them.

Later we learned from several villagers that these parents were known for constant vicious fighting between them, to the point where the husband sometimes beat his wife. I was present to watch them as their child died. Their anger was first placed on Jesus, "Why did you not save him?"

And then they began to soften in their grief. They turned to one another and wept on each others' shoulders and supported one another in a way they had not done in a long time. Together they arranged for their child's funeral and burial. Somehow in their grief they rediscovered their love for one another.

That Jesus did not save the child is what led to this healing between the parents. I don't think He tried to figure that out. It seemed to me more that He followed His heart. I asked Him later, "Did you know what would happen?"

He said, "No one can ever know what will happen."

I asked Him, "Why did you not save the child?"

He said, "What does it mean to save the child? How would the child live with such angry and violent parents? The spirit will simply move on and go where it will go. When it is ready to return it will return."

These stories are about faith. Watching those parents weep and the child move into release from his pain and eventually die, there was fostered in me a deep faith that things happen as they need to happen. When we believe, 'Thy will be done,' and move according to our innate wisdom and compassion, things happen as they need to.

This is not just faith for the individual to learn, but a more encompassing faith in understanding the suffering of mankind. There are seemingly tragic conditions augmented by natural circumstances, as well as the more vivid and distasteful ones that man creates with free will − often very unskillfully. For every painful situation, either in ourselves or in others, there is always a hidden lesson of value for us all. In our impatience and lack of faith, the lesson is more often not revealed or understood until after the pain has subsided.

If that pain is lodged deeply in a person, it will fester and turn to anger. With anger in the forefront of one's consciousness it is nearly impossible to have faith and see the lesson being offered. When Jesus felt sadness and compassion, it was often because He knew the limitations of some people, and that they would have to experientially suffer the consequences of their pain and that of others so as to learn the lesson that was being offered to them. As humans, we would be wise to observe the examples Jesus lived and to follow His path as best we can. Eventually we will discover the faith and open-heartedness that says, 'I am the instrument. If I seek and allow, God will work through me. Thy will be done.'

We stayed in that village for several weeks. For many days the parents who lost their child came to Jesus with anger, and each time He returned their anger with kindness, simply acknowledging the depth of their grief. Toward the end of His stay they came to Him and said, "You have given us a gift. Through all the years of our son's life he was sick, and we blamed one another.

The man said, "I blamed my wife that she didn't take care of him." And she said, "I blamed my husband that he did not provide well enough to let us buy medicines and pay for prayers. You have given us a gift; you have given us back to each other and a second chance to love one another."

Jesus did not look at the child's soul plan to see if the child came to give the parents this healing. He did not try to figure it out on that level. He simply was as present with the child's pain as He could be, and as loving and non-judgmental with the parents as He could be. He let His heart guide Him and He understood Himself to be a vehicle for Divine love and wisdom.

Thy will be done. At this He was the master. I can not adequately express my gratitude to Him for the ways He taught me these lessons of faith.

Thirty-Three

Whenever I traveled with Jesus, it was a wonderful opportunity just to walk and talk with Him. The days were filled with wonder and learning. Jesus literally mirrored Divinity to those who followed Him. Sometimes a person would come along, who, in contrast to Jesus' shining radiance, saw only their own darkness, and to that Jesus would attend with love. Far more often, Jesus would draw out a person's radiance so that they became capable of love and kindness to a level which they had never thought possible. He never shamed anyone for their fears or confusion. He was more like a mirror, allowing us to reflect off Him; and thereby, seeing the best of whom we could be.

Here is an example. Leprosy in those days was much dreaded. There was no cure and the disease was contagious. Therefore, people were terrified of coming in contact with lepers. Those who had the disease were ostracized and forced to leave their families and towns; and to live alone among themselves in constant pain and struggle.

One day as we walked, from high up among the rocks came the cry of a woman in pain. She did not cry out specifically to us; I doubt she even knew that we were passing by. Without even breaking His stride, Jesus turned off the path and headed toward her. I, and several others, followed Him up a steep path among the boulders. We came upon five people in a small cave, all of them lepers. Except for Jesus, we froze in our tracks. There was a mother with her teenage daughter, and they were both quite taken-over by the disease. The daughter wept in pain as her mother held her.

Jesus did not pause. It was clear that He had no fear for Himself, as we did for ourselves. He asked for water and clean cloths, but there were no clean cloths. They brought Him water and again He said, "I need clean cloths." And as He said It, He looked me in the eyes. I knew He would not have shamed me, nor would He have forced me to do anything. But His direct gaze drew me so deeply into Him, that my fear simply vanished. I then discovered something in me that was far more fearless; and more loving and noble than I had ever realized. I removed my soft cloak, which was quite clean. I not only brought it to Him, but I was able to stay there with Him.

He gave me a beautiful smile and said, "Thank you." And then again, as our eyes met I saw the Essence of Divinity in Him reflected back to me, and I knew that I could stay and help. Jesus asked me to cut my cloak into strips and I saw in His face such hope and beauty. I then found it easy to take the knife from a leper and cut the garment into strips for bandages. I also helped wash and bandage the wounds. Later we shared food with them and sat by the fire for some time. The young woman lessened her weeping. She came and sat next to Jesus and He took her hand, as a father to His child. As her pain decreased, she also ate.

I have no doubt that Jesus could have instantly cured all of these people. Yet, He did not want to create a scene of specialness around Him, but rather to demonstrate the power of human love, and that it was possible for ordinary people and not just saints. He wanted to empower people, not dis-empower them and cause them to feel helpless before His great Mastery. That time with the lepers was magic for me. It was the first time I was not ashamed of my fear or selfishness. I have thanked Jesus often for being such a mirror of human divinity.

Some people did not like Jesus because, due to their own fears and insecurities, they needed to believe in a leader who would exhibit great power over negative situations. People who were consumed by their fears did not want to hear His lessons of Love. In such people, Jesus reflected to them their own lack of love. They felt ashamed of themselves and then raged at Him for bringing such a teaching to the world. His truth and clarity of heart left them nothing to hide behind. He knew this, yet in His great mercy He still offered His truth to the world; and His compassion to those who were not ready for truth.

Thirty-Four

We were traveling in another place. We had settled for the night in a wilderness area up in the hills. Far in the distant valley, we could see the firelight of a village. It was dusk and we were eating our dinner when some rough-looking men approached. They saw us gathered there; one of them recognized Jesus and said,

"Ah, it's the one they call the Rabbi." Jesus had been eating and sat there with some bread in His hand. One of them came up and grabbed Him by His shirt and snatched the bread from Him and ground it into the dirt. "Aren't you going to stop me?" he taunted. "Oh, that's right, turn your cheek!" And then some of them began to pull food away from the rest of us, trying to get us to fight, but we would not.

My son Mark, who was about ten at the time, was with me. The leader of the men grabbed him and literally lifted him off the ground. I felt Jesus' restraining hand on me. Jesus rose and approached this tall and hefty man who towered over Him while holding my son up in the air.

Jesus looked at him and said in a voice balanced with stern command and true compassion. "Put him down!" He looked at this man, not with hatred or pity, which only would have pushed him further, but with a Divine Love that no one could miss. Again He said, "Put him down." Jesus helped that man get in touch with the divinity within himself, perhaps for the first time ever.

This man's attitude of negativity began to dissolve right in front of us. Tears came into his eyes. He put the lad down gently.

Before he could say anything, Jesus said to him, "Do not be ashamed. Lifting him in that way, it was your fear and anger speaking. Setting him down, it was your love speaking. And you have just proved which is the greater voice in you." The man only nodded. Then he and the others went on their way.

In the Presence of Jesus, I saw grown men weep. Not all; some would push away with their anger. They were not ready to see. For a mirror to work, one must be ready to look. Jesus did not manipulate people; He did not force anyone to be where they were not. But for those who were ready to choose love over fear, He provided the mirror.

Thirty-Five

One day as we walked with Jesus, we came upon a group of seven well-to-do men, beating up three other less-fortunate men. Jesus did not pause. He walked up and laid a hand on the arm of one of them and His other hand on the arm of another.

"Why do you beat them?" He asked.

"They stole from us. They came during the night and we have just now caught up with them."

Then Jesus asked, "What do you hope to gain by beating them?"

"They are thieves and they must be punished."

Jesus asked sincerely, "Why would anyone steal from you if he were not terribly confused or hungry; fearful or needy? How would it be for you if you did not have money to feed your families or warm clothes to wear? What if you had been raised to hatred and treachery instead of kindness?" The minds of these men were programmed by the social conditions of that time.

"But they deserve to be beaten," said one of them. "It's their fault that they are afraid and hungry. They too could be prosperous if they lived differently."

"Could they?" Jesus asked. "If you grew up without a trade, without kindness in your lives, where would you learn what you needed to know in order to survive?"

As the talk went on, Jesus kept inviting them to open their hearts in compassion to these other men.

"Is not their suffering enough punishment?" said Jesus. "They came to you hungry and when they leave you they will still be hungry. Is this not enough punishment?"

There is that in every human which wants power and revenge, for through those things, we can feel ourselves to be strong and in control; therefore, safe. And, there is also in every human the heart of compassion, without which we would not be human. So seldom do we touch the compassionate heart that we may forget that it exists. In Jesus' face shone compassion for both sides; for those who were needy and desperate, and for those who were afraid that their power, honor and safety would be violated. Those who were doing the beatings were afraid that if they let some tiny niche for compassion into their armor, that it would begin to disintegrate and then their whole sense of safety would be gone.

Jesus then said, "You want to be safe. All men want to be safe. But safety cannot be built with a hateful heart. Safety can only be built on love. Only in your genuine love for these men will you find safety, which they also so desperately seek."

One of them said, "But how can we love them when we hold our anger as our strength and protection?"

"Do you know these men?" Jesus asked.

"We have seen them here and about. They live in shacks beyond the village."

"Do they have families?" Jesus asked. Nobody knew.

"Do you have families?" Jesus asked the robbers. Some of them nodded, yes. "Do you have means of supporting yourselves?" They nodded, no.

Jesus turned to the seven men and asked whole-heartedly, "Since they are in need, would you be willing to give of yourselves to ease their need? And not to just give them some food but also a sheep that is ready to bear young and some seeds with a bit of land? Would you also help them build a warmer shelter for themselves and their families?" With great inspiration He asked, "Who will do this with me?"

Of course we, His followers all nodded. Two, and then three of the seven nodded slowly.

"Then let us go now and see what they need."

Now, the three who had been beaten were quite uncomfortable. They were proud and did not want charity. So Jesus had not only to deal with those who were defending themselves with strength, but also with those who were in need and felt they could only meet their needs through strength.

Looking at the three, Jesus asked them, "How would it be if you had a way to feed your family without having to steal for it?" They looked at the ground and shuffled their feet. "You know you are capable men," He told them. "Do you want to live your lives harming others? I do not ask you only to receive. To support yourselves would mean an end to your harming others, and this would be a true gift to all." In the Divine content of His language, Jesus inspired all of them to be the best they could be.

In the end, four of the seven accompanied us to the place where these less-fortunate men lived. They talked to the men's children. They saw the squalor in which they lived. They were filled with sadness that they had so much while others suffered. In all of these men, from both sides, Jesus awakened a sense of their own deepest truth: to live together in love and cooperation, and to touch within themselves generosity and kindness. Jesus helped them to soften their fears enough to give and receive, for both are equally difficult to do.

Thirty-Six

While I was walking through the hills with Jesus and others, a boy who was carrying a lamb with a broken leg, came to greet Him. The boy was crying because of the lamb's obvious pain, and because he was afraid it would die. Jesus took the lamb into His arms. There were some shepherds about and also a group of people who were walking with Him.

He said to the boy, "Come walk with us. We'll see what can be done."

Certainly Jesus could have healed that lamb instantly, straightened the leg and handed it back to the boy, and then word would have quickly spread that Jesus had performed a miracle. Instead He held the lamb in His arms and we walked, and the mother sheep walked along with us. Dusk came.

Jesus said to the boy, "Stay with us. Have supper and sleep here with us. We'll see how the lamb is in the morning."

The lamb drank from its mother's milk. It was laid on the ground and we all went to sleep. In the morning the lamb was found standing squarely on all four legs and sucking from its mother. The boy was filled with wonder.

"Look what you did!" he exclaimed.

Jesus said, "No. It is not I, who has done this, but the wonder of life has restored itself in this lamb."

Jesus was saying that He was simply the channel through whom the Divine had worked, thus bringing the lamb to its own healing. He neither took credit nor denied. He just indicated that the lamb had found his healing, through the wonder of life.

Thirty-Seven

Another time there was a child who was brought to Him. The child had fallen into a fire as a baby and lost his vision in the accident. His face showed signs of the burns. The child was placed in Jesus' arms.

Jesus simply asked him, "Do you wish to see again?"

"Yes."

"Do you believe I can heal you?"

"Yes."

He held the boy in His arms so tenderly and put His hands over the boy's eyes and face. In a few moments, when He took His hands away, the terrible scars were healed and the boy could see.

Some of those who had accompanied the boy were outlaws and made their livelihood upon other's pain. They were very frightened when the boy was returned to them healed.

They asked Jesus, "What do we owe you for this?"

"Oh, nothing, nothing," was all He said.

This upset them because it put them in His debt. As it was dusk, He invited them to sit by the fire and talk. He treated them courteously and respectfully. He asked them questions and heard their responses. He led them to look at the choices that created harm for themselves and others; but He did this so gently that it was as if the questions had arisen in themselves, as indeed they had. The healing of the boy was a doorway through which He found access to their hearts.

Thirty-Eight

During His travels Jesus frequently encountered flocks of sheep. He knew that I was a shepherd. As we walked a path one day, a young man came to us.

He recognized Jesus and said, "My sheep is having difficulty giving birth."

And indeed we could hear her crying nearby. We went to her. There was no shepherd with her and the lad did not know what to do. I offered to reach into the birth canal and feel the position of the body. What I felt was a lifeless mass. This baby was dead within the mother.

I said, "The lamb is dead," and the lad began to weep.

"I'm not sure," Jesus said.

He held His hands over the mother's abdomen and just sat there focused for a few minutes. Then the mother began to move again, pushing in labor and delivered a live lamb.

I looked at Jesus and said, "But I was so sure it was dead."

He just smiled at me and said, "He was not yet alive, but now he is. Let us leave it at that."

I already loved Jesus and I had seen this Divine Power move through Him with His desire for healing and God's goodwill. In this act there was the quality of pure compassion, and pure love for the lad.

Thirty-Nine

One time, in the winter, I was walking with Jesus through the hills between two villages. It was late afternoon, but already dark. A light snow was falling. As we descended the hills and were about two miles from the village we heard a crying noise and then an animal snarling. Jesus immediately stepped off the path toward the sounds. Over a small rise ahead of us we saw a mother goat on the ground with a very young baby close to her. Several large wild mountain cats were circling them. The mother had a broken leg and was emaciated from extreme hunger. She had continued to nurse her baby until her milk ran out. She was dying. Now these wild cats had come, seeking food.

I remember the way Jesus picked up the baby; the way the mother looked at Him with a sense of trust, knowing that He would not harm her baby. With our human presence the cats pulled back into the shadows. Jesus opened His cloak and tucked the baby in against His warm skin, then closed His cloak over it. "Build a fire," He asked.

By the time the fire was going the mother was dead. It seemed that once she had realized her infant would be cared for, she could then release her hold on life. The cats began to move in closer, wanting meat. They got so close that Jesus stood up, still holding the baby to His chest and said, "No! This one is mine. You will not harm it." But He also understood their hunger and natural instinct. He had us cut the carcass into pieces and toss them to the cats. He then had us mix some water and bread into a paste. I remember how He sat there with this baby creature's head peeking out from His robes. He dipped His fingers into the warm paste and repeatedly held it to the creature's mouth. And so this small animal took in nourishment. He had no less compassion for the wild cats than for the baby's hunger. I will always remember how He held that baby goat and His statement, "This one is mine." Jesus was a metaphor for Love, He literally was Love, and His Love embraced us all.

Jesus was not overly sentimental. If the mother goat had been severely injured to the point of death, He might have killed her Himself and offered her to the cats. If she was going to die; then it would have been more humane to kill her quickly, than to have her living body torn to shreds. If we had been able to splint her leg and create a litter for her, He would have done that, then carried her. If He saw that the cats were hungry but not starving, I presume He would have given them all of our food and then chased them away.

He understood that compassion does not choose one over the other; that all are equal. If, instead, one of the wild cats were injured and had a baby to look after, I think somehow Jesus, with His powers, would have found food for them. He did not prefer to do miracles of that sort in front of crowds of people, but He was certainly capable of doing so. In fact, He could have healed the mother goat when we first saw her. But He did not 'play God'. He did not choose to make life and death decisions that would hold one being as more valuable than another. He would not have sacrificed one to feed another unless, in the natural order of things, that one was dying.

Forty

Jesus taught me to deal with my confusion about feelings of anger and desire for revenge. One evening I found Him with some of His disciples, gathered around a fire. Often, in fair weather, Jesus would politely refuse the hospitality of sleeping in someone's home, preferring instead to sleep outdoors on beautiful nights. On this night the sky was clear and the stars were brilliant.

I asked permission to come and sit by the fire with them and Jesus granted it very happily. Though I knew Him well, I was unable to talk at first. Part of what had brought me to seek Him was that He talked of forgiveness, and I had had something happen in my own life that I did not know how to forgive.

I told Jesus that I had a beloved brother who was very dear to me. He was good and kind and gentle and yet he was brave, and would never let another be hurt if he could help it. A while back my brother was with a friend when outlaws came to rob him. They were somehow misinformed that our friend had much gold. In truth he had none and lived a simple life with few possessions.

The outlaws burst in saying, "We want your gold!"

Our friend just opened his hands and said, "I have no gold."

They then said to my brother, "Leave. You have nothing to do with this."

But my brother would not leave. He stepped in front of his friend to help protect him and said to the outlaws, "He has no gold. It is you who should leave." So they beat my brother severely.

From then on my brother was in a coma, barely alive. It seemed to me that he would soon die and I was filled with anger. My greatest wish was to find them and kill them; to make them pay for what they had done. And yet I loved Jesus, who taught everyone to turn the other cheek; and to forgive and love one another. This is what led me to Him that day. His words resonated in my heart and I felt that I could not simply condemn these men without first telling Jesus my story and hearing His advice.

Initially I hoped that He would tell me that those men deserved to die. I hoped that He too would be angered, yet I also hoped He would relieve me of my own anger and pain. When I came into His presence and felt His strength, gentleness, and kindness, I knew that His answer was going to steer me away from anger. I was afraid of His answer because I did not think I was strong enough to do what He would ask of me.

My whole being had been caught-up in condemnation of those men. Jesus listened to my story. I trembled to tell it for fear of His judgment. I wanted our friendship to continue, but I feared that He would hear my anger and send me away.

He just listened. When I was finished He said to me simply, "I hear how great your anger is. It is very painful for you." As He said this, He looked at me with the kindest eyes you can imagine, completely free from judgment.

And I said, "Yes, that is true."

And He said, "What do you want to do?"

I said, "I want to kill them, and this wish is so against what I have ever felt or learned."

He noted, "You are suffering. Will that ease the suffering?"

My first response was, "Yes."

He said, "What then after you kill them? Will that bring your brother back to health? Will that give you peace?" And then He looked me in the eyes and spoke again, "Hatred shrouds the compassionate heart. But that heart is still here." With those words He gently touched my chest and I could feel the possibility of forgiveness.

"Who are they?" He asked. I told Him they were a band of poor men who lived in the hills; that they were lazy and did not work, but stole for a living. I told how widely feared and hated they were. But, that as a band, they were strong and people were afraid to go after them. "Do they have children?" He inquired. I did not know. "Do you think they enjoy their life?" I didn't know. "Have they ever been taught to find what they need without hurting others?" Again, I did not know.

But His questions awakened a realization in me that these men were not monsters; they were men who had gone wrong. I realized that without the gentle care of my own parents, I might have become one who hurts others to fulfill my own needs. A certain spark was ignited in my heart; a spark that had always been there. His presence and non-judgment brought it to life. It was the seed of compassion.

For three days I walked with Jesus and the others. Occasionally He would seek me out and say, "How is the anger today?" and then He would talk with me about it. He taught me not to disrespect my anger; but also not to hold it and use it as a tool to harm others. He taught me that if I disrespected my own anger, then I disrespected myself. He led me to see that I did not have to get rid of the anger to find my compassionate heart. He helped me to touch Love rather than hatred, and to rest in that.

At the end of three days I had to go back to the work of tending my sheep. He asked me, as I was ready to depart, "What will you do? Do you still want to kill them?"

I said, "I don't know what I will do because I now know that I can no longer kill them. Yet, they have hurt my brother and he may die soon and they continue to harm others. I do not know what to do."

He said to me, "Why don't you just pray that an answer will come; that some solution will come, and then see what happens? Hold the desire for healing in your heart and talk with your friends about it too, and see what happens."

I returned to my home. It was not as easy to keep that Love accessible without His presence, but it was there. I found that as long as I practiced with my anger as He had taught me, and as my father and brother had also taught me, I could stay in touch with the Love as well. I began to talk to people about what He had told me. They in turn began to see how anger and even hatred could be present with Love and Light.

Several months later, I was on a hillside in the night with my sheep. Noise was coming from the village down below and I hurried down to see what was the matter. Others came down from the hills all around as well. We saw that these same outlaws had again come into the village, with knives drawn. We assumed they were looking for objects of value to steal. Many villagers armed with staffs and sticks were chasing them away.

One of the outlaws seemed to be carrying something in front of him and placed it on the ground as he fled. I came to it first. To my surprise it was a child, a young boy. Why he carried his child with him we did not understand. Why he had left the child was still more of a mystery. Some people simply turned away, but several of us picked up the boy and made the decision to follow these bandits to their home and return him.

The boy was emaciated and dirty, but not afraid of us. It was clear that he had been raised with kindness. We came into the hills carrying the boy. Some of their lookouts shouted to us, "Who are you?"

We said, "We are returning a child," and they permitted us to pass.

Finally we came to their leader. Their dwellings were really just shallow caves. I held out the boy to him and said, "Is this your son?" and tears filled his eyes.

He said, "All of our children have died. They have starved. He is the last one. I left him on purpose so he would not die."

These were the fierce beings that I had hated. They had done wrong and had killed. Nothing justifies such wrongdoing. Yet when we looked more closely we saw that some of them were cripples and others were blind or sickly. It seemed that they knew no other way to survive but to steal. And there weren't that many of them, perhaps a dozen men and women. Jesus was right. The spark of Love was there in my heart. Seeing these ones as human beings, it was impossible to hate them.

We decided to find ways to help them grow food. We gave them some seeds and sheep and helped to teach them the skills they would need for these tasks. They could not understand why we would do this. They said, "But we have stolen and killed."

And I was able to look at one and say, "Yes. You hurt my brother." And although Jesus was not there to say it, I know His words would have been, "And now you are my brother and I cannot harm you in return."

Jesus did not merely preach forgiveness, tolerance and love, but He also led each of us to find that Love in our own hearts. He opened the way to that discovery by reflecting His own enormous loving kindness and non-judgment. He was Light and Love, and that is what He drew out in all beings.

Forty-One

The penalties for wrong-doing in those days were severe. Someone caught stealing would have his hand cut off, which often meant starvation for him and his family. Generally, there was not enough food for people and life was difficult. Often people stole because they were starving.

I had been walking with Jesus for several days. Upon entering a small village we became aware of a skirmish. A man had been caught stealing a loaf of bread. Commonly in small villages the police, judge and jury were all one person. The villagers called upon such a person to solve this problem. Looking only at the surface of the situation, he asked, "What happened?"

"He stole bread," replied one of the villagers. That was the end of the investigation. He was not given a fair trial or asked why he had stolen the bread.

This man was weeping and crying, "My children, they will starve!" No one bothered to answer him. These people were not evil; they simply had not learned kindness and understanding of others. With closed hearts, they took protection behind the law. So we witnessed a tragic ending to this robbery. The man was literally held down and his hand was cut off. We saw to our horror that the other hand had previously been cut off and was nothing but a stub. They simply cut his remaining hand off and walked away, leaving him lying on the ground to cope with his trauma; to live or die.

We came to assist him immediately. Jesus quickly removed part of His robe and used it to bandage the wound. He knew how to stop the spurting blood by applying pressure. The man was in physical agony and terrible emotional pain as he said, "My children, my children! What will I do?"

We carried him off with us a short distance where we settled for the night and built a fire. Through the night he was feverish and in and out of consciousness, but he kept saying, "My children, my children!" We found someone who knew him. His wife had previously died and he had two young children. Someone was sent to fetch the children. They were found alone and frightened in the dark. The children were safe for the moment. The man's stub would heal, but he no longer had hands. If he could not provide for his children they would probably starve.

This man was very bitter and filled with hatred. As a youth he had done something foolish and lost his right hand. That left him feeling diminished and helpless. Instead of cultivating what skills he could with his left hand he sunk deeply into his helplessness. He began to truly believe that the only thing he could do for a living would be the most menial of jobs, and when such was not available he would steal. He knew the consequences if he got caught. He had a choice but his heart was not capable of seeing that choice. He was too consumed with anger and hatred. Undoubtedly he had suffered much as a child and had never come to see his divine potential.

However, this man had one special gift. He had a lovely voice; one of the most clear and beautiful voices I have ever heard. Sometimes in the evening he would sing to us. In those moments his pain would soften and he would sing.

We stayed there for a few days. As soon as he was strong enough, this man and his two children were invited to travel with us. Often people brought food for Jesus and His followers, and so the children were easily fed. After a few weeks this man approached Jesus with his head hanging down and said very quietly, "It is time for me to go. I am a burden to you."

"Where will you go?" asked Jesus.

"I don't know, but it is time for me to go." It was his fear and sense of unworthiness speaking. Because he felt so unworthy it was very hard for him to accept the gift of Love.

Jesus looked him in the eyes and actually tilted the man's chin up to make eye contact and said, "If you go, you will deprive me of your singing. Your music is so beautiful. It so deeply inspires me. Please stay."

The man agreed to stay for a few more days. Each evening and sometimes as we walked, Jesus would ask him to sing. But then the man's sense of unworthiness would return and he would say, "Now it is time for me to go." And again Jesus looked at him and said, "But you would deprive me of your singing. You would deprive us of your beautiful music. Please stay."

The time came for me to leave and I did not return for several months. When I returned I could barely recognize this man. With his stubbed arms he had learned to carry things and do certain chores for himself and others. He was no longer helpless. There was a Light shining from him that had been completely missing. This Light glowed because Jesus had faith in him; He had seen this man's divinity and mirrored it back to him. In doing so, He helped the man believe in that divinity and discover it for himself.

The man's amputations had helped to teach him. Sometimes he would actually hold out his stubbed arms and look at them and call them his teachers. All it took was one person to take the time to look deeply inside him with Love and see the whole man. Jesus helped him see his anger, his fear and his faith, which indeed led him to find his truth. Jesus could see this in people because of who He was. The power of His Divinity shining out into the world, was life-changing to whomever encountered it.

Forty-Two

Jesus understood His power. He understood His Divinity. And yet, He was humble because He understood that every being has that same power and Divinity; and simply has not yet realized it. He did not come just to teach us of His power and Divinity but also of the Divinity of All That Is. In His teachings He did not set Himself above others.

He was not afraid of His power or His authority. He was not afraid to speak from that authority. But He did not command anyone to believe Him; rather, He spoke His own Truth and asked others to find the resonance of that truth in themselves. He did not lecture or instruct through words nearly as much as He modeled that which He hoped others would emulate. He modeled Love in human relationships. He modeled loving kindness, respect and reverence. And also, He modeled power.

I would not say that He worked miracles; so much as He skillfully used Divine Power. He knew the innate perfection of All That Is and He knew how to bring that perfection to manifestation. But Jesus did not want people to focus on His healing powers. In my times with Him I occasionally heard Him say He felt He had not fully succeeded in His mission, because so many people misunderstood Him and invested Him with special power. People looked up to Him and prayed, "Heal me, touch me, save me," rather than seeking His teaching to help them do this for themselves. He allowed others to place Him on a pedestal insomuch as it was a part of their own learning process. But even so, whenever possible His work was to empower others and bring their awareness to their own Divinity.

One time, while encamped outside a village, we heard a tale of robbers in the village market place. That evening as we sat around our fire a man crept forward from the shadows, literally on his hands and knees. He crawled up to Jesus and confessed that he was a thief and said, "Save me, save me," for if the villagers found him they would have his hands cut off. He said, "They will cut my hands off, and then my family will die. I will no longer be able to provide for them."

Jesus asked him, "Why did you not think of this before you stole?"

The man was very ashamed. He said, "I could not support myself in any other way. My father was a thief. I do not know of any other way to support my family. I have been stealing all of my life. I know it is wrong but this is all that I know how to do."

Jesus asked him, "Have you any skill or craft?"

The man looked down and shook his head.

"You learned thievery from your father," Jesus said. "What did you learn from your mother?"

"How to weave," the man said. "When I was a child I would help her weave. As her hands became arthritic I did much of her weaving for her. She was very talented."

"And did people buy her woven material?" Jesus asked.

"Yes," the thief replied.

In those times sheep were commonplace and many people owned some. Consequently, much yarn was spun and woven. We were encamped in the yard of a friend's family. There were too many of us to sleep in the house, and no need for shelter on such a fine night. Jesus turned to the householder and asked, "Do you have a loom?"

"Of course," said the owner.

Jesus brought the thief inside and sat him before the loom. The man proceeded to weave a very beautiful pattern of fabric, an unusual pattern with several stitches overlaid so the yarn, though only one color, took on a lovely texture.

"Do you know other textures, other patterns?" asked Jesus.

"Yes."

So Jesus planted the idea in the man that he was not a failure and not devoid of ways of supporting himself, and that he could indeed provide not only for his family but also provide beauty for the world.

"Go home," Jesus told the man. "Use your mother's loom." When I come through this village again I want to see you weaving."

The man began to weep.

The man had re-connected not only with his original creative expression, but also his sense of divinity, which was woven into the fabrics he made. When we happened to pass that way about six months later we stopped in to visit. The man was weaving exquisite fabrics and they were very much in demand. He sold enough to comfortably support his family; he also gave many away as gifts, especially to those whom he had robbed.

Several weeks later in a different village, I saw the man in the marketplace with his fabrics. Another village vendor pointed to him and said, "That is the one who stole from me last year." Although the fabric man no longer looked the same – he looked more pleasant and happy now – other vendors who had been robbed also recognized him and said, "Oh yes! Yes, that's him! You're right!" They grabbed him and said, "Are you the one who robbed us?" It took enormous courage for him to admit that he did, and he knew the consequences he might suffer.

The custom then was to deliver justice swiftly. They all agreed that he was guilty. And then one who was wearing a shawl that this man had made for him said, "But look what he has learned to do with his hands." As they looked around they saw that many of them were wearing fabrics that this man had woven. They realized the man who had robbed them was in the same body, but he had become someone very different. They could not, would not cut off his hands so long as he dedicated himself to creating such beauty, and promised not to rob ever again.

I was very blessed to be present. That night after the market had closed, the man came to Jesus and took his hands and knelt before him. He was in tears. He said, "You have saved me. You have given me my self-worth."

And Jesus said to him, "No, your self-worth was always there. You made the choice to cast off your fear and the stealing it engendered. You have brought forth your own divine beauty, creativity and love. It is you who developed this. I only reminded you that you could do it."

The man had not considered this before. He looked at his hands that he had been so afraid would be cut off and said, "Just as God created the world, so these hands also can create beauty." He looked at his hands with wonder and renewed appreciation.

Jesus said to him, "Yes, and the beauty flows from your heart through your hands. It is the Divinity in your heart that holds the sacred blueprint of that beauty."

The man sat there weeping, holding out his hands, and Radiance shone from him that I had not seen in him before. Within that radiance I recognized not only his, but every soul's self-worth and divinity.

Forty-Three

What follows is a story of a man who thought that he was evil. He had grown up with cruelty and scarcity; and with poverty of both body and spirit. This was not uncommon in those days. One day this man joined us as we were traveling with Jesus. The man was unkempt in his body appearance and kept his eyes cast on the ground. I saw Jesus attempt to speak to him a few times. The man just muttered a few words and looked away. So Jesus walked beside him quietly, not forcing His words upon the man.

That night we were welcomed at the home of an old friend of Jesus'. It was a lovely evening and we chose to sleep under the stars in his courtyard. During the night I saw the man get up and walk quietly into the house. Curious, I followed him, watching from a distance. In the darkness inside, there was only the shadowy light of the fire. There was a box where ornate silver and gold coins were kept. The man looked around to be sure that nobody was watching. But he could not see me through the doorway in the next room. So he filled his pockets while still looking around. He also took a lovely jeweled knife and a beautiful scabbard with a jeweled handle.

I wasn't sure what to do. I did not feel that I could allow him to rob our friend. I hesitated because I was not sure what was best for this man. Finally he turned away from the box and as he came toward me I stepped forth.

But at that same instant, much to my surprise, Jesus stepped forward from another room. The man looked at me. I looked at Jesus. There was greed and fear in the man's expression.

Jesus stepped forth and said, "Do you really want to take those things?" The man looked down at the ground. He could not meet Jesus' eye.

"I am an evil man," he said.

"Have you stolen before?" Jesus asked. The man shook his head no. "What will you do with what you have taken?" Jesus continued.

"I don't know," the man said. He had not thought that far ahead. It was just there and his greed drove him to do it.

"Are you hungry? Is you family in need?" Jesus asked.

"No family," the man muttered. "I am alone. I am not in need. I am just an evil man." Jesus stood there and simply looked into the man's eyes. The man said again, "I am just an evil man," and Jesus held his gaze. The man looked down. Jesus held his hand under the man's chin and gently raised his face, commanding his eyes.

"Is that all there is to you?" said Jesus. "Tell me when you have been kind to another." The man withdrew himself again and looked down at the ground. He repeated, "I am just an evil man." Again Jesus lifted the man's chin and looked into his eyes. "Tell me of a kind deed you have done in the recent past."

Slowly the man spoke, "I gave money to the beggar in town."

"Yes," said Jesus. "Tell me more." For over an hour He invited the man to recount numerous kind and generous things he had done. And each time Jesus said, "Is this the doing of an evil man?" the man paused. "Well... does that sound like the doing of an evil man to you?"

Finally the man admitted, "Well, maybe not."

What Jesus was doing was inviting this man to see that which he had not allowed himself to see, which was his own goodness. The man was so caught in the negativity that came through him that he focused all his attention on that, which kept him from seeing his goodness.

At the end of their discussion Jesus simply said to the man, "I'll go back to sleep now. I suggest that you do the same." He did not tell the man to return the stolen items. Just, "It's time to sleep." Jesus turned from the man and went back to His place to sleep. Taking my cue from Him, I did the same. But I saw the man watch us leave and then I could hear him putting everything back in the box. He then walked out of the house and was about to leave through the gate when Jesus got up and came to him again and said, "Where are you going?"

"I have shamed myself. I must leave."

"No," Jesus said. "You have shown me your goodness. You have shown the true side of your nature. Please stay and see how much more of your true nature will blossom."

The man was a bit surprised and asked, "You are really inviting me to stay?"

"Of course," said Jesus.

"But you don't even know if I returned everything."

Jesus simply said, "That will be up to you." He offered the man the sleeping space and blanket next to Him by the fire and then Jesus lay down. The man made another trip into the house and I heard one more piece drop into the container and then he came out and lay down by the fire.

The man traveled with us for the next few days. He became courteous and went out of his way to be kind to others. He offered others the first and best food. One could see that he was not doing these things as a need to purify himself, but simply out of his own goodness. God's Light began to shine from him. Before I left to tend to my sheep I needed to ask him a question.

"Do you still believe you are an evil man?" I asked.

"No," he said, smiling. "No. That evil man is gone. My fear created him, but he is gone."

This is what Jesus came to teach; that each being has his or her own Divinity, and how to bring it forth and express it to the world. This is His gift to you, and it is the gift that you may give to the world and to each other.

Forty-Four

One time when I was traveling together with Jesus and others, our path brought us near a community of lepers. A woman came near hoping to get our attention. Her daughter, who was also a leper, was giving birth. But the baby would not come because it was a breach birth. No one there was knowledgeable enough to help her.

Jesus and I went immediately up into the cave where the daughter lay in pain and fear. Others there had boiled water and provided clean cloths, but beyond that they were helpless. As a shepherd I knew how to turn a lamb positioned awkwardly in the birth canal. I am certain that Jesus could have fixed this in some way, but He turned to me and said, "I have watched you deliver lambs in an awkward position. What should we do?"

Even though I had encountered lepers before with Jesus, I was not fully comfortable around them. I was conditioned with the belief that they were unclean and my wisdom and compassion were blocked by old fear and limitation. So I hung back a bit. If Jesus had commanded me, certainly I would have done what He asked. But He understood that this was not a matter of command. Yes, command would save the baby, but He had a second priority. This was a matter of helping me grow past that place of fear and limitation in myself, and the willingness to do that had to come from my own heart.

Jesus was asking me to allow myself to be touched with the blood and flesh of this woman who was a leper. He was telling me that it was only my fear that put me in danger; that I truly could not be harmed here. It is not that I could not become ill, though that would be unlikely, but that the deepest essence of me could not be harmed.

Looking at Jesus, I knew that if He had my skill in assisting with difficult births, He would not hesitate. Suddenly all of my old fear and sense of limitation burst open and evaporated. There was no more leper; just a woman giving birth to a child. So I was able to turn the child to a position in which it could come forth. In a few minutes I had a beautiful infant in my hands and it had no sign of disease.

Jesus preferred to allow healing to be natural, without signs of His intervention. Several weeks later, as I was returning to my sheep and family I came by this same leper colony. I went up to see how the baby was. Their living area was a number of caves and a community hearth. There were about two dozen people of various ages there.

As I came into their space there was a Radiant Energy. They recognized me immediately and the mother held the baby for me to see. But it was not the baby who captured my attention, but the mother, whose body had been covered with scabs and sores. Now her face was clean. She was missing some fingers but her hands were also clean of sores. A man stepped forth and showed me that his entire body was healed.

"Did Jesus do this?" he asked.

"I don't know," I said. "I don't know how it happened, but I think that your love and faith have drawn it forth." That was enough confirmation for them.

Assuredly Jesus had a part in their healing. But nobody can be healed unless they are ready to be healed. It is the recognition of your own Divinity, which is also connected to that ever-radiant Divinity in Jesus that brings forth the healing.

Forty-Five

One time a man joined us on the trail, for dinner. The night passed and the next morning he had left with our food and robes. Two days later we came upon him. He expected that we would beat him. Instead Jesus said, "My brother, you don't trust me. You run off in the night instead of asking for what you need. We are happy to give you what you need. Please sit with us." And Jesus fed him.

We noticed that his leg was injured and had become infected. Jesus said, "Let me look at your leg. It looks very sore." Jesus offered to wash it and then put some ointments on it. Then He said, "Please don't rush off tonight. Stay with us so we can help take care of your leg and let it heal." The man was there in the morning. He ate breakfast with us and then walked with us.

It took about a week for the leg to heal. Each day Jesus talked with the man and saw to it that his needs were met. Something wonderful happened during those days. We came upon an older man who was injured and could barely walk. It was an old and permanent injury and the man walked with crutches and hobbled. The first man's leg infection was healing, so Jesus said to him, "Can you help our elder friend here? It would be so helpful to him if he could put his arm around somebody's shoulder. With that assistance, it would surely help him walk."

Jesus gave the man something positive to do, which was really a way to give of himself. The days passed. Although the man with the crutches could not walk quickly, he now had support. He wanted to walk with us; he wanted to hear Jesus. Jesus made it possible for the man who had been a thief to find that part of himself that found real joy in being of service to another, and it was wonderful to see this man blossom.

We then came to the city of our destination. The reformed thief had planned to stay there, and Jesus asked him, "What are you going to do here?"

The man said, "I am going to see who I can help in this city." He eventually found others of a like mind and created a mission of sorts; a place where people who were homeless or without food could come and find goods. He went out and literally begged of those who were wealthier to give food, blankets and so forth.

Months later when we came back through that city this man had become a great help to others. His life was completely reformed. You can imagine what would have happened if we had beaten him with sticks when we first knew him as a thief, as many people would have done. He would have simply moved deeper into the negativity that had been conditioned in him.

All of you have negativity conditioned in you by the pain in your lives. Only love will heal it. Your own negativity to yourselves will not heal it in you, and your negativity to others will not heal it in them. But when you see the Divine, each in the other, you come to know that you can live in love and share that love with others.

Forty-Six

Jesus was familiar with the practice of meditation. He was able to move freely into a state of deep concentration, but did not indulge Himself in it for an escape. He recommended that practice, as well as deep presence in each moment and prayer, to others. For Jesus, meditation was part of His own training that went into making Him what He was, but formal meditation was not part of what He taught to others. Always His teachings to others were on compassion and forgiveness; to open your heart to love; to know God's presence within each Being; and to relate to everything within this Divinity.

I felt myself to be a disciple of Jesus and a follower of the Path that He traveled. What He taught always spoke to my heart more than anything or anyone I have ever heard, anywhere. I tried to follow His teachings and to share them with others. In this way I became very much a follower of His and at a certain point in my life I left my shepherding to be with Him. I was not one of His primary disciples. I simply had a very deep love for Jesus ever since the time of our childhoods.

A great beauty in all that Jesus inspired and healed in others, was that they rarely actually knew that Jesus did it. And in effect, He did not do it. He simply showed a situation wherein healing and love might happen and trusted the best in each to seek it out.

Inviting kindness so that others could see and then use it was a great talent of His. He never claimed credit. He did not want others to bow before Him or to worship Him. He simply wanted to invite their loving hearts to open; to get them to know this Divine Essence within themselves. And because He reflected it so profoundly, you could not be with Him without experiencing your own Divinity unless you were quite deeply enmeshed in darkness.

I think this, as well as the deep love that He inspired, is what eventually led to His crucifixion. It all depended on which side of the fence of awareness you were sitting upon. Some people condemned Him because His words of truth and love so threatened everything they had been brought up to believe, and hold onto, in a usually fear-based philosophy. Other people loved and adored Him because His words of truth and love ignited their own passions and senses of Divinity to the point where they were even willing to defy the social and religious standards of that time in order to follow Him.

Those who could not see their Divinity reflected in His, experienced shame. Jesus did not see this as any one's personal fault; He knew it as their conditioning. Rather, He had the courage to do what was needed in the face of human fear and confusion. He opened a door. Many Beings were able to walk through that door and others were not yet ready. Perhaps they needed to experience that depth of shame and linger in the shadows with themselves before they were ready to express the Light. Herein is His willingness to die, without blaming others, but having already offered forgiveness to others and challenged them to ask it of themselves. He offered His own life as witness to the inner Divinity of every Being.

Forty-Seven

The last time I saw Jesus before the crucifixion, we sat together for some hours. He said to me, "My path takes me in a different direction than I thought it would. I knew I would not be a shepherd as you are, but I thought I would be a figurative shepherd; that I could live a simple life and share with people these teachings of Love and Divinity and God. But that way seems to be closing to me."

Jesus had taught me that no way was ever closed, so I asked Him, "What do you mean, it is closing? Can you now just open it? You have taught me to never believe in ideas of limitation."

His words to me were very powerful. He said, "Each of us comes to birth with an intention, a path, and it may not always be an easy or pleasant one; not the one we expected. But we can follow it. We can manifest anything, but the heart of Love must be at the center of our manifestation. Love tells me now that the path I accept goes through the darkness of unknowing, and I must follow it. This path is not about my will, but our Father's Will and I know this is also my deepest Will, no matter what any fear that I have may say to the contrary."

His faith was so powerful that it was more like a knowing. This deep clarity of His faith was so powerful for me. He knew His life would end in radical change for that in Him that was fully human. I think most of you understand that He did not die. The human known as Jesus died to the world. Then Jesus lived on in a much richer, deeper form; a deeper expression of His divinity. But the personality self that said, "I want to be safe; I want it my way," had to die. And He could see through the grasping at that end. All of His training and experience and years of perpetual faith to God led Him to understand the task that lay before Him.

I think He could take this final step so gracefully because it is what He had practiced all His life. Not just the release of negative energy or the surrender of the ego, but also the integration of the human and the Divine. And this is not just for Him. All of you share this birthright of Divinity. What He did, you can do. Each of you is capable of expressing that same Radiance and Light out into the world, and this is truly why each of you is here. You are constantly learning to do this with more skill; to bring more and more loving kindness, wisdom and compassion into your earthly movements and thoughts.

Jesus had a wonderful, penetrative Radiance that was more than faith. It was the purest of Love. Through that Love, He was willing to give everything to do the work He came to do. He taught us about our Divinity through His deepest expression of His own Divinity, all pouring out from Him in that incarnation. Through the way He accepted His death, that final expression of His Love and Divinity moved me more than any prior experience I ever had with Him. It led me to shake loose that fear within myself.

You may wonder why Jesus did not choose to escape His death on the cross, knowing that He could have. There is an interesting balance here. We must identify with and open our hearts deeply to the personal self, the relative human, because this is how we develop compassion. But we must also know the greater Being of which we are a part.

I was not present at His death, but I knew He had been captured and would be put to death. Officials asked me if I knew Him and I must admit that I denied Him, out of fear for myself. The tremendous guilt and fear I felt about that led me away; as far away as I could get at that point. It was not until several weeks later – having spent that time of isolation in prayer and meditation – that I understood what I had done and what I needed next to do.

I then joined those who had been His followers and who continued His teachings. I found that there were many others who also felt guilt and had also learned the true depth of His message of forgiveness through that guilt, and the necessity to forgive ourselves. From this perspective, His death was His final gift to me in that lifetime.

In the end, many of those who opposed Him were also the ones who were most shaken by His death. It was then that they finally saw His pure expression of Divinity which had moved among them. And now He and that Divinity were gone. It was then that they realized how much they wanted what He had; they wanted Him and that sense of Divinity back. And now they would have to work even harder to uncover that Divinity in themselves. They saw their terrible loss. Thus, many who had opposed Him came to mourn Him when He had died.

Jesus truly taught me that I am divine and that my divinity is in everything, should I choose to see it. He awakened that knowledge in me and in countless others. You do not need His physical presence. His pure and undiluted Essence is always here among you. This Divine Energy, or Holy Spirit, is everywhere. If you can not see it in yourself, then turn and look at your neighbor, or at a child.

Each Being has the ability to reflect God's Divinity. But to reflect it you must first know it in yourself, and you must open the eyes of your heart in order to see it. Then, you must have the courage to make the choice to enact that goodness in the world, even if your fear, pain, greed or anger are still present. It is in this way that you can best honor Jesus and what He came to teach.

When you come to know that Divine Essence in yourself, you will be forever changed. You will feel, as is mentioned in the Bible, truly reborn. Your negative emotions and thoughts do not suddenly cease to exist, but they do begin to lose their power. Each time you decline to give attention to the negativity that arises in you, you plant a new and more wholesome seed which literally replaces the older one. This new seed enhances the way of kindness and love and leaves fear behind.

If you ask that Divine consciousness be with you, He will come to you in some form or another. You always have free will. It is your asking that opens the doorway. Then you again have the free will to step through or not to step through. He will hold the door open for as long as you need Him to. But you must ask. The significance of your asking is what makes it genuine and real for you. It strengthens the part of you that aspires to goodness, purity and love. So you must open your heart fully to everything in yourself. This is the challenge: to love and forgive all. Embrace yourself and this love with compassion. Vow to not add negativity in the world, but to move beyond it and sever your identity with it. When you seek to do this, Divine Guidance will always be present and ready to help.

Afterword

by Aaron

Can you imagine what it would mean to die in the agonizing way He did when He so easily could have prevented it? This was the supreme test for Him. In transcending His human fear of death and not engaging His powers to stop it, He points the way for all Beings. It is His Mastery of His centeredness in the Divine in which I stand most in awe. I feel so much gratitude toward Him for what He taught and for His willingness to be in human form and reveal the wonders of God on our level. Here was a Being Who had full God-Realization and yet still walked the earth. He came into the incarnation from that full realization and He was able to maintain and express it on earth, even with all the flaws and temptations of being human. It is such an inspiring statement of human potential. When you cease to be a slave to your ego then you can begin to more fully express that Divinity in all of your life. This is the gift you can give back to Jesus, directly; and through giving it to all other beings as well.

Jesus has chosen to stay available to us. He is able to use the mental body to communicate on a verbal level. He is also able to communicate Divine Energy. Out of His great Love, He remains available, as He did in the time after His death, in the Resurrection. This is His path. If you seek Him, He is there.